Introductory
Descriptive
Chemistry

THE GENERAL CHEMISTRY MONOGRAPH SERIES

Russell Johnsen, Editor

Florida State University

Gordon M. Barrow (*Case Institute of Technology*)	THE STRUCTURE OF MOLECULES
Fred Basolo (*Northwestern University*), Ronald C. Johnson (*Emory University*)	COORDINATION CHEMISTRY
Gregory R. Choppin (*Florida State University*)	NUCLEI AND RADIO-ACTIVITY
Werner Herz (*Florida State University*)	THE SHAPE OF CARBON COMPOUNDS
Robin M. Hochstrasser (*University of Pennsylvania*)	BEHAVIOR OF ELECTRONS IN ATOMS
Ronald C. Johnson (*Emory University*)	INTRODUCTORY DESCRIPTIVE CHEMISTRY
Edward L. King (*University of Colorado*)	HOW CHEMICAL REACTIONS OCCUR
Edwin M. Larsen (*University of Wisconsin*)	TRANSITIONAL ELEMENTS
Bruce H. Mahan (*University of California*)	ELEMENTARY CHEMICAL THERMODYNAMICS

Introductory
Descriptive Chemistry

Selected Nonmetals, Their Properties and Behavior

Ronald C. Johnson

Emory University

1966

W. A. BENJAMIN, INC.   New York   Amsterdam

INTRODUCTORY DESCRIPTIVE CHEMISTRY:
Selected Nonmetals, Their Properties and Behavior

Library of Congress Catalog Card Number 66–28908
Manufactured in the United States of America

*The manuscript was put into production on June 9, 1966;
this volume was published on November 11, 1966*

W. A. BENJAMIN, INC.
New York, New York 10016

Editor's Foreword

THE TEACHING OF INTRODUCTORY CHEMISTRY becomes each day a more challenging and rewarding task as subject matter becomes more diverse and more complex and as the high school preparation of the student improves. These challenges have evoked a number of responses; this series of monographs for general chemistry is one such. It is an experiment in the teaching of chemistry which recognizes a number of the problems that confront those who select textbooks and teach chemistry. First of all, it is recognized that no single book can physically encompass all of the various aspects of chemistry that all instructors collectively deem important. Second, it is admitted that no single author is capable of writing authoritatively on *all* of the topics that are included in everybody's list of what constitutes introductory chemistry. Finally, it recognizes the instructor's right to choose those topics which he considers to be important without having to apologize for having omitted large parts of an extensive textbook.

This volume, then, is one of approximately fifteen in the General Chemistry Monograph Series, each written by one or more highly qualified persons very familiar with the current status of the subject by virtue of research in it, but also conversant with the problems associated with teaching the subject matter to beginning students. Each volume deals broadly with one of the subdivisions of general chemistry or areas directly impinging on it and constitutes a complete entity, far more comprehensive in coverage than is permitted by the limitations of the standard one-volume text. Taken together

v

these volumes provide a range of topics from which the individual instructor can easily select those which will provide for his class an appropriate coverage of the material he considers most important.

Furthermore, coverage of a number of topics only recently being considered for introductory chemistry courses, such as thermodynamics, molecular spectroscopy, reaction kinetics and mechanism, atomic spectroscopy, photochemistry, and biochemistry is or will soon be available. In every instance a modern structural point of view has been adopted. The emphasis is on general principles and unifying theory, but with adequate reference to experiments.

These materials will have other uses also; selected volumes can be used to enrich the more conventional course of study by providing readily available inexpensive supplements to standard texts. They should also prove valuable to students in other areas of the physical and biological sciences needing supplementary information in the field of chemistry pertinent to their own special interests. Thus, students of biology should find the monographs on biochemistry, organic chemistry, coordination chemistry, and reaction kinetics particularly useful. Beginning students in physics and meteorology will find the monographs on thermodynamics and atomic structure rewarding. Teachers of elementary science will also find these invaluable aids to bringing them up to date in the various branches of chemistry. The monograph on nuclei and radioactivity should prove useful to anyone interested in the application of radioisotopes to experimental problems.

Each of these monographs has several features which make them especially useful as aids to teaching. These include a large number of solved examples and problems for the student, a glossary of technical terms, and copious illustrations.

It is hoped that titles will continue to be added as new areas come into the purview of introductory chemistry. Suggestions for additions to the series will be welcomed by the editor.

RUSSELL JOHNSEN

Tallahassee, Florida
April 1965

Preface

THE TREND in textbooks on introductory chemistry at both the high school and college levels has been to gradually expand the coverage of the principles of chemistry. This has been accomplished by reducing the space allotted to descriptive inorganic chemistry. This trend is a natural and necessary consequence of our increasing understanding of the factors responsible for chemical behavior. Some recent texts have gone to the extreme of omitting all but incidental discussions of descriptive chemistry. I believe that a modern introduction to descriptive chemistry is desirable in the early stages of the training of all chemistry students. Therefore, I have written this text on descriptive inorganic chemistry which I hope will serve as an interesting and broadening supplement to introductory "principles" texts. A related purpose is to balance courses based on some of the variety of paperback texts which are now available for beginning students.

This text presents the chemistry of a few nonmetallic elements in more detail than is generally found in introductory texts. I hope that, in probing deeper into the chemistry of a few elements, it has been possible to convey to the reader a little of the excitement which is always present on the frontiers of science. The behavior of these few nonmetals has been used to illustrate the generalizations on which a modern understanding of all elements is based.

The task of presenting the essentials of descriptive inorganic chemistry in a small text or in a limited number of pages of a larger book is difficult, particularly in view of the rapid increases in our knowledge of the behavior of inorganic materials. This text seeks to solve the dilemma of too much material to cover in too few pages by selecting from much worthwhile chemistry a few topics which meet the criteria of importance, interest, and utility in the presentation of generalizations. Even with such criteria, the choice of material is largely arbitrary. Many topics which certainly deserve mention have been omitted. Nonetheless I hope that the material which is included will maintain or increase the reader's interest in chemistry and will encourage him to study the behavior of other elements on his own. The text does endeavor to present generalizations which will allow the reader to make reasonable predictions of the behavior of substances which have not been dealt with. It also suggests source materials for further study.

The use of this book should be most effective for readers who are familiar with the type of chemical theory presented in modern general chemistry texts. The presentation assumes a familiarity with the electronic theory of atoms, elementary bonding theory, and the use of half-cell electrode potentials. Simple concepts of heat and energy are used, but a background in elementary thermodynamics is not assumed. Persons with this background, however, should be able to grasp the thermodynamic significance of the more qualitative information presented. There was no need to use calculus in this text. A more sophisticated mathematical-physical chemistry approach would have significantly limited the usefulness of the book to the average college student. The level of this book should be consistent with its use by college students who have some background in beginning college chemistry and high school students who have had a sound year course in chemistry. It may also be suitable for other courses which do not have a physical chemistry prerequisite.

I would appreciate suggestions for the improvement of this text and reports of student reaction toward it. I want to thank my wife, Dr. Susan Johnson, for her many helpful suggestions.

Ronald C. Johnson

Atlanta, Georgia
August 1966

Contents

ix

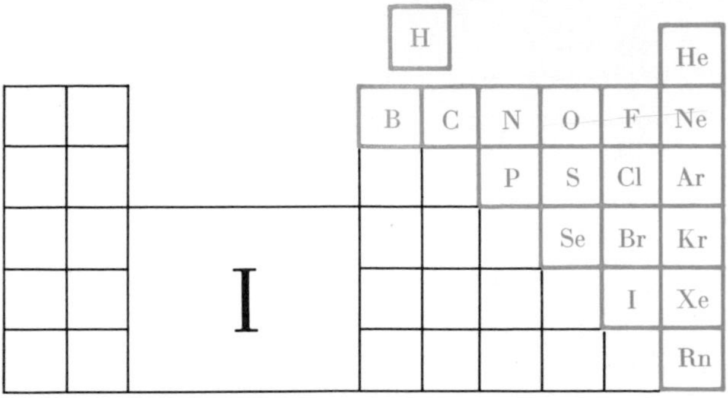

H

He

B C N O F Ne

P S Cl Ar

Se Br Kr

I

I Xe

Rn

Nonmetals

1–1 INTRODUCTION

THE CHEMICAL ELEMENTS have been classified as metals, non-metals, and semimetals. This book presents an introduction to the chemistry of a few of the nonmetals and points out generalizations which are useful in the study of all the elements.

The nonmetals and many of their compounds are important for human survival as well as in a wide variety of industrial processes. Oxygen is an obvious example of a nonmetal necessary for life as well as one used in huge quantities in industry. (Over 7 million tons of oxygen were produced in the United States in 1965.) Water, a compound of two nonmetals, is equally important to plant and animal survival and is a vitally important industrial chemical. The fertilizer industry, the products of which are necessary to produce sufficient food for the world's mushrooming population, deals primarily with the nonmetals nitrogen and phosphorus. Over a million tons of liquid ammonia (NH_3) are produced for agricultural purposes each year in the United States, as are millions of tons of phosphate-containing fertilizers. Nonmetals have a host of other uses which are vital to each of us.

Rapid advances are being made today in nonmetal chemistry. One of the most stimulating scientific discoveries in the last decade

Periodic table of the elements

	I A	II A	III B	IV B	V B	VI B	VII B		VIII		I B	II B	III A	IV A	V A	VI A	VII A	
1 H 1.008																		**2** He 4.003
Period 2 (2)	**3** Li 6.940	**4** Be 9.013											**5** B 10.82	**6** C 12.010	**7** N 14.008	**8** O 16.0000	**9** F 19.00	**10** Ne 20.183
Period 3 (2 8)	**11** Na 22.991	**12** Mg 24.32											**13** Al 26.98	**14** Si 28.09	**15** P 30.98	**16** S 32.066	**17** Cl 35.457	**18** Ar 39.944
Period 4 (2 8 8)	**19** K 39.100	**20** Ca 40.08	**21** Sc 44.96	**22** Ti 47.90	**23** V 50.95	**24** Cr 52.01	**25** Mn 54.94	**26** Fe 55.85	**27** Co 58.94	**28** Ni 58.71	**29** Cu 63.54	**30** Zn 65.38	**31** Ga 69.72	**32** Ge 72.60	**33** As 74.91	**34** Se 78.96	**35** Br 79.916	**36** Kr 83.80
Period 5 (2 18 8)	**37** Rb 85.48	**38** Sr 87.63	**39** Y 88.92	**40** Zr 91.22	**41** Nb 92.91	**42** Mo 95.95	**43** Tc* [99]	**44** Ru 101.1	**45** Rh 102.91	**46** Pd 106.4	**47** Ag 107.880	**48** Cd 112.41	**49** In 114.82	**50** Sn 118.70	**51** Sb 121.76	**52** Te 127.61	**53** I 126.91	**54** Xe 131.30
Period 6 (2 18 18 8)	**55** Cs 132.91	**56** Ba 137.36	**57** La to **71** 138.9	**72** Hf 178.50	**73** Ta 180.95	**74** W 183.86	**75** Re 186.22	**76** Os 190.2	**77** Ir 192.2	**78** Pt 195.09	**79** Au 197.0	**80** Hg 200.61	**81** Tl 204.39	**82** Pb 207.21	**83** Bi 209.00	**84** Po* 210	**85** At* [210]	**86** Rn* 222
Period 7 (2 18 32 18 8)	**87** Fr* [223]	**88** Ra* 226.05	**89** Ac* 227	**90** Th* 232.05	**91 92** Pa* to **103**													

Nonmetals Semimetals Metals

4f series:

58 Ce 140.13	**59** Pr* 140.92	**60** Nd 144.27	**61** Pm* [145]	**62** Sm 150.35	**63** Eu 152.0	**64** Gd 157.26	**65** Tb 158.93	**66** Dy 162.51	**67** Ho 164.94	**68** Er 167.27	**69** Tm 168.94	**70** Yb 173.04	**71** Lu 174.99

5f series:

91 Pa* 231	**92** U* 238.07	**93** Np* [237]	**94** Pu* [242]	**95** Am* [243]	**96** Cm* [248]	**97** Bk* [247]	**98** Cf* [251]	**99** Es*	**100** Fm*	**101** Md*	**102** —*	**103** Lw*

*All isotopes are radioactive.
[ ] Indicates mass number of longest known half-life.
Note: The small figures at far left show electron distribution in preceding noble gas.

Figure 1-1   Periodic table of the elements.

2

involved the reaction of the nonmetal xenon with platinum hexafluoride and later with fluorine to produce the first compounds of the noble gases. This development, of which we will have more to say later, came as a surprise to most chemists since we had been taught that xenon and the other noble gases were completely unreactive.

1–2 PROPERTIES OF NONMETALS

The classification of chemical elements into metals, semimetals, and nonmetals is both difficult and somewhat misleading. Certain properties are characteristic of metals and others, characteristic of nonmetals. However, many elements exhibit intermediate behavior and a regular gradation from metal-like to nonmetal-like elements is observed.

The periodic table arranges the chemical elements in terms of their electronic configurations. Since the electronic configuration of an element largely determines both its chemical and physical properties, the periodic classification is also of prime importance in discussing the metallic or nonmetallic nature of an element. Historically the grouping of elements in terms of their atomic weights and chemical and physical properties (which included their metallic or nonmetallic nature) led to the development of the periodic table.

Figure 1–1 presents a periodic table in which an arbitrary classification of the elements into metals, semimetals, and nonmetals has been made. The metals are found on the left and bottom of the table, the nonmetals on the right and top. Semimetals separate the metals and nonmetals.

The metallic or nonmetallic nature of an element is best indicated by certain physical properties. The most obvious properties which help us to classify an element as a metal or nonmetal are its physical state, appearance, and malleability and ductility.[1] All elements which are gaseous at room temperature are nonmetals.

---

[1] A malleable substance can be flattened out by rolling or beating; a ductile substance can be drawn into a wire.

Liquid or solid elements may be metals or nonmetals. Polished pieces of metals other than copper and gold are gray to white in color with a few showing tinges of blue, pink, or yellow. The nonmetals exhibit a variety of intense colors (from the yellow of sulfur to the deep violet of iodine). They can be obtained as crystals, in which form they are shiny and transparent; however, most are commonly seen as dull powders or lumpy substances. Solid nonmetals are either hard and brittle or soft and crumbly. Most metals, in contrast, are malleable and ductile. These readily apparent physical properties allow one to distinguish between most metals and nonmetals. However, for a number of elements, particularly those in the vicinity of the semimetals in Figure 1–1, these properties do not provide an unambiguous classification and other properties must be considered.

1–3   PERIODIC PROPERTIES

The periodic table is the most useful single concept in developing an understanding of the descriptive chemistry of an element. On the basis of the position of an element in the periodic table one can predict its metallic, semimetallic, or nonmetallic character, its common oxidation states, the formulas of many of its compounds, and many other properties. *Periodic properties* of elements are those which one can predict on the basis of the position of an element in the periodic table. A characteristic feature of such properties is that the elements in the lower left-hand corner of the periodic table (cesium, Cs; francium, Fr; and radium, Ra) show one extreme value of the property; elements in the opposite corner (fluorine, F; helium, He; and neon, Ne)[2] exhibit the other extreme. Intervening elements exhibit a somewhat regular gradation in the property. For example, cesium, francium, and radium are definitely metals whereas fluorine, helium, and neon are nonmetallic.

---

[2] A relatively common but explicable exception to this rule is the observation that fluorine rather than helium often shows properties with the greatest contrast to francium. Examples of such behavior and the reasons for it will be presented later in this chapter.

	H (g)				He (g)

Li 30	Be 40		B 10^{-10}	C (graphite) 0.1	N (g)	O (g)	F (g)	Ne (g)
Na 60	Mg 60		Al 100	Si 10^{-9}	P (white) 10^{-15}	S 10^{-20}	Cl (g)	Ar (g)
K 45	Ca 70		Ga 6	Ge 10^{-6}	As 10	Se 10^{-9}	Br small	Kr (g)
Rb 20	Sr 10		In 30	Sn 0.1	Sb 8	Te 10^{-3}	I_2 small	Xe (g)
Cs 15	Ba 5		Tl 15	Pb 15	Bi 3	Po —	At —	Rn (g)

Figure 1–2   Relative conductivities of the representative elements.

Intervening elements include the other metals and nonmetals and the semimetals.

The conductivity of an element, its structure, ionization potential, electron affinity, and the acid-base properties of its oxides and hydroxides are all examples of periodic properties. Let us now consider each of these properties in more detail, note the value of the periodic classification, and see that these properties are indicative of metallic and nonmetallic behavior.

Electrical Conductivity

The electrical and thermal conductivities of an element are good measures of its metallic character. Metals are good conductors whereas nonmetals are nonconductors.[3] Figure 1–2

---

[3] Carbon in the form of graphite is an exception; the conductivity of this element can be related to its unique bonding and structure.

presents the relative conductivities of the nontransition elements at room temperature. Between the highly conducting elements on the left in the periodic table (metals) and the poorly conducting elements on the right (nonmetals) in Figure 1–2 lies a group of elements with intermediate conductivities. Most of these elements were classified as semimetals in Figure 1–1. The elements with intermediate conductivities are examples of semiconductors. A useful property of all semiconductors is their increased conductivity when hot. This property is being used in a wide variety of space age electronic devices. It is difficult to determine accurately the conductivities of the elements in the crucial semimetal region. This is true because minute traces of certain impurities will enhance the conductivities of these elements by several powers of 10. Analogous to semiconductivity is the photoconductivity exhibited by selenium; the conductivity of this element increases when it is exposed to light. A characteristic feature of the conductivity of metals is that it decreases as the metal is heated. This effect has been attributed to thermally induced disorder in the metal which hinders electron flow.

Crystalline Structure

Elements on the left-hand side of the periodic table (metals) are observed to have structures in which each atom has a large number of nearest neighbors and in which the atoms are packed together in a manner which minimizes vacant space in the lattice. Structures in which the maximum number of atoms of the same size are packed in the smallest volume are called *close-packed structures;* the two such arrangements are illustrated in Figure 1–3. Virtually all metals crystallize in one of the close-packed structures or in an atomic arrangement called the body-centered cubic structure (Figure 1–3). The atoms in this structure are quite tightly packed (but not close-packed—see the problems after this chapter). Each atom has eight nearest neighbors and six additional neighbors at a slightly longer distance. In the close-packed structures each atom has twelve nearest neighbors. Notice that in each structure all atoms occupy equivalent sites.

Crystals of the noble gases (elements far from metals in the periodic table) have close-packed structures like those of metals. However, there are striking differences between metals and noble gases. The highest boiling noble gas (Rn, b.p. $= -62°C$) has a boiling point 419° below that of the lowest boiling metal (Hg, b.p. $= 357°C$). This difference is a reflection of the fact that the forces between atoms in metallic solids (metallic bonds) are much greater than the forces between the molecular units (atoms, in the case of the noble gases) in nonmetals (*van der Waals forces*).

In the structures of other solid nonmetals each atom has fewer nearest neighbors than the eight to twelve found in metals. In general the atoms in a nonmetallic solid are much less densely packed than those of a metal. The arrangement of atoms in nonmetals results primarily from the number of atomic orbitals and electrons available for covalent bond formation. Hydrogen ($1s^1$) and the halogens ((inner electrons) ns^2np^5) each have only one low-energy, half-filled orbital, and therefore form only one covalent bond. In the gas phase these elements exist as diatomic X_2 mole-

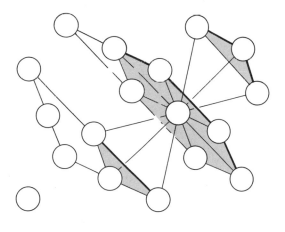

(a)

Figure 1-3 The structures of metals: (a) cubic close-packed (face-centered cubic), (b) hexagonal close-packed, (c) body-centered cubic. In solids each atom touches its nearest neighbors; in these drawings and others in this text atoms are separated for the sake of clarity. (See page 8 for parts b and c.)

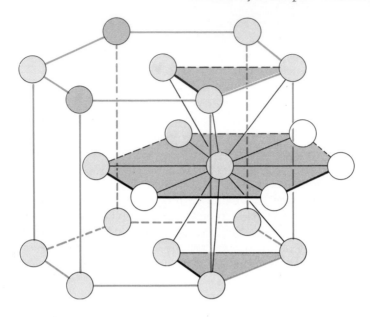

(b)

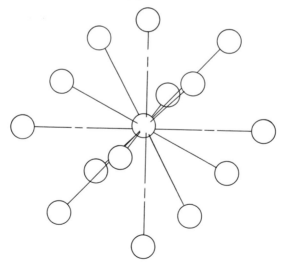

(c)

Figure 1–3 *(continued)*

cules. Oxygen ($1s^2 2s^2 2p^4$) and nitrogen ($1s^2 2s^2 2p^3$) are able to form two and three covalent bonds, respectively, since oxygen has two half-filled p orbitals to use in covalent bond formation and nitrogen has three. They also tend to form multiple bonds with themselves and therefore exist as $N\equiv N$ and $O\!=\!O$ in the gaseous state.[4] These diatomic covalently bound molecules are also present in the solid state in which they are held to neighboring molecules by van der Waals forces. The high volatility of these elements (all are gases at room temperature except Br_2 and I_2) indicates that the forces between molecules are weak. As the number of electrons in these compounds increases, the van der Waals forces and the boiling points increase. In the solids of all nonmetals each atom is relatively close to the atoms to which it is covalently bonded and much further from neighboring atoms in other molecules. For example, in chlorine the centers of covalently bonded chlorine atoms are separated by 1.99 A,[5] whereas the centers of chlorines in two neighboring molecules are separated by 2.79 A.

The elements directly below oxygen in the periodic table have two nearest neighbors in the solid state; those below nitrogen have three nearest neighbors, and the nonmetals below carbon have four.[6] The number of nearest neighbors in each case corresponds to the number of half-filled orbitals which can be provided by the atom for covalent bonding. Fragments of the structures of some of the elements in these families are illustrated in Figure 1–4. The fragments illustrated are either parts of covalently bonded infinite networks or consist of units packed and held together by van der Waals or other forces.

Boron has a structure unique from that of any other substance. One might characterize it as a nonmetallic structure on the basis of the fact that the boron atoms are not tightly packed; each boron

---

[4] The bond between two oxygen atoms in O_2 has the strength the length of a double bond; however, a completely acceptable Lewis dot structure with a double bond cannot be written.

[5] An angstrom unit, A, is 1.00×10^{-8} cm.

[6] Carbon, like oxygen and nitrogen, has a strong tendency to form multiple bonds with itself. In graphite, the stable form of carbon, each atom has only three nearest neighbors, but these three atoms are attached with four bonds.

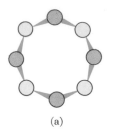

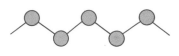

(a)

(b)

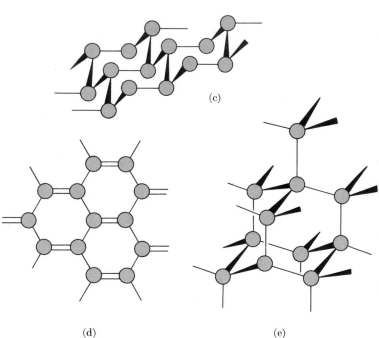

(c)

(d)   (e)

Figure 1–4   Fragments of the structures of some non-metallic solids: (a) sulfur and one form of selenium, (b) selenium and tellurium, (c) the stable forms of phosphorus, arsenic, antimony, and bismuth, (d) graphite—the stable form of carbon, (e) diamond—the other structure for carbon.

atom has only six nearest neighbors (fewer than the eight to twelve found in metals—see Section 3–1).

In general one finds that the semimetals have structures with some features of both metals and nonmetals. For example, arsenic, antimony, and bismuth each have three nearest neighbors in their solids. However, each atom also has several other neighbors which are not much farther away; this is particularly true of the heaviest elements. The layer and chain structures of these elements make this easily achieved by simply packing adjacent layers and chains tightly together. In bismuth the three nearest neighbors are at 3.10 A; three additional bismuths are situated at 3.47 A with six more at a longer distance. The structures of arsenic, antimony, and bismuth can be considered to be very distorted, close-packed configurations with increasing distortions in the lighter elements.

Some elements form two or more types of crystals, some of which are metallic and others nonmetallic. For example, tin crystallizes with a nonmetallic diamond-like structure at low temperatures. In the familiar form which is stable at room temperature each tin atom has six nearest neighbors and the element is relatively dense and metal-like in appearance and properties. The stable form of solid selenium consists of long chains of selenium atoms (see Figure 1–4a, b); this form is metallic in appearance and is photoconductive. Crystallization of selenium from carbon disulfide solutions yields an unstable nonmetallic solid which is similar to sulfur and contains Se_8 rings.

Ionization Energy, Electron Affinity, and Electronegativity

The three related properties ionization energy, electron affinity, and electronegativity are all periodic properties. The *ionization energy* (or ionization potential) of an element is the smallest amount of energy necessary to remove one electron from an atom of the gaseous element—the energy required to produce reaction (1-1).

$$E(g) \rightarrow E^+(g) + e^- \qquad (1\text{-}1)$$

The smallest amount of energy required to remove a second electron is called the second ionization energy, and so on. Electrons are most readily removed from elements on the left-hand side of the periodic table and less readily removed from those on the right (see Figure 1–5).

The *electron affinity* of an element is the energy change during reaction (1-2).   About 80 kcal/mole are liberated when halogen

$$E(g) + e^- \rightarrow E^-(g) \tag{1-2}$$

atoms combine with electrons.   The electron affinity of the metal lithium is about 12 kcal/mole.   It is difficult to determine electron affinities; therefore, accurate values are not generally available. However, it appears that elements on the right-hand side of the periodic table have larger electron affinities than those on the left.

H 314 2.10							**He** 567 —
Li 124 0.97	**Be** 215 1.47	**B** 191 2.01	**C** 260 2.50	**N** 335 3.07	**O** 314 3.50	**F** 402 4.10	**Ne** 497 —
Na 118 1.01	**Mg** 176 1.23	**Al** 138 1.47	**Si** 188 1.74	**P** 254 2.06	**S** 239 2.44	**Cl** 300 2.83	**Ar** 363 —
K 100 0.91	**Ca** 141 1.04	**Ga** 138 1.82	**Ge** 187 2.02	**As** (230) 2.20	**Se** 225 2.48	**Br** 273 2.74	**Kr** 323 —
Rb 96 0.89	**Sr** 131 0.99	**In** 133 1.49	**Sn** 169 1.72	**Sb** 199 1.82	**Te** 208 2.01	**I** 241 2.21	**Xe** 280 —
Cs 90 0.86	**Ba** 120 0.97	**Tl** 141 1.44	**Pb** 171 1.55	**Bi** (180) 1.67	**Po** — 1.76	**At** — 1.90	**Rn** 248 —

Figure 1–5   The ionization energies (in kcal/mole) and electronegativities of the representative elements. The values are taken from E. J. Little and M. M. Jones, "A Complete Table of Electronegativities," *J. Chem. Ed.*, 37, 231 (1960).

It is not unreasonable that elements which hang tightly onto their own electrons might also seek to gain an additional one. The exception to this generalization is the observation that the noble gases have little or no tendency to accept additional electrons.

The periodic change in both ionization energy and electron affinity can be related to the fact that in an atom all electrons in the same shell are on the average the same distance from the nucleus. Therefore in lithium ($1s^2 2s^1$) the single $2s$ valence electron is attracted by the charge of about one nuclear proton; the charges on the other two protons are largely "neutralized" by the two $1s$ electrons which are between the valence electron and the nucleus. In fluorine ($1s^2 2s^2 2p^5$) each of the seven valence electrons ($2s^2 2p^5$) are attracted by an estimated nuclear charge of about $5+$. Two of nine nuclear protons are "neutralized" by the two $1s$ electrons; the remaining electrons are quite ineffective in screening each other from the nucleus and thus each experiences an attraction from most of the remaining nuclear charge. Therefore any one of these electrons is much more difficult to remove from the atom than is the one electron from the lithium atom. With respect to electron affinity, an additional electron captured by a fluorine atom would fit in a $2p$ orbital and would also be attracted by a nuclear charge of about $5+$; an electron captured by lithium would be attracted by only about one nuclear charge. In a noble gas such as neon the second shell is filled and additional electrons would have to be added to the third shell which is farther from the nucleus. In this case essentially all of the electrons in the first and second shells would be between it and the nucleus and would "neutralize" most of the nuclear charge. It would therefore be bound weakly, if at all.

The *electronegativity* of an atom has been defined by Linus Pauling, formerly professor of chemistry at California Institute of Technology and the recipient of both a Nobel Prize in chemistry and a Nobel Peace Prize, as the ability of an atom in a molecule to attract electrons to itself. Electronegativity, although obviously related to electron affinity, is a different and useful concept. The definition of electronegativity is not an operational one, that is, it does not indicate how measurements of the property should be made. As a result electronegativity values for the elements have been proposed from studies using a variety of methods; reasonably consistent results were obtained. A method suggested by Professor R. S. Mulliken of the University of Chicago averages the ionization energy and the electron affinity of an element (1-3).

Electronegativity $= 0.0085$(ionization energy

$$+ \text{ electron affinity}) \quad (1\text{-}3)$$

The constant 0.0085 is used to convert the values calculated using energies in kcal/mole to the absolute scale used by other workers.

Electronegativities of the representative elements are presented in Figure 1–5. The metals are seen to have low values (0.86–1.82), whereas the nonmetals have larger ones (2.01–4.10). Elements with electronegativities in the neighborhood of 2.00 tend to be semimetallic.

Acidity of Oxides and Hydroxides

The basicity and acidity of oxides and hydroxides of elements are periodic properties. Elements near fluorine have the most acidic oxides and hydroxides; those near francium have the most basic oxides and hydroxides. The acidity of an oxide or hydroxide of an element therefore is related to the metallic character of that element; the oxidation state of the element is also an important factor. Equations (1-4) and (1-5) give examples of an acidic hydroxide and an acidic oxide. Boron hydroxide is more commonly

$$B(OH)_3 \xrightarrow{H_2O} B(OH)_3OH_2 \rightleftarrows H_3O^+ + B(OH)_4^- \quad (1\text{-}4)$$

$$SO_3 \xrightarrow{H_2O} H_2SO_4 \xrightarrow{H_2O} H_3O^+ + HSO_4^- \quad (1\text{-}5)$$

known as boric acid and it produces aqueous solutions which are weakly acidic. Sulfur trioxide, an oxide of a nonmetal, produces very strongly acidic solutions. An example of a basic oxide is sodium oxide. This metallic oxide produces strongly basic solutions (1-6).

$$Na_2O \xrightarrow{H_2O} 2NaOH \xrightarrow{H_2O} 2Na^+ + 2OH^- \quad (1\text{-}6)$$

Oxides of many elements are insoluble in water. Their acidic or basic character can be evaluated by determining whether they will dissolve in acids or bases. For example, antimony(III) oxide (Sb_2O_3) is insoluble in dilute HNO_3 and in pure water but can be dissolved in basic solutions. The solution process can be visualized as resulting from the neutralization of the acidic oxide by the basic solution. On the other hand, bismuth(III) oxide (Bi_2O_3) is insoluble in alkaline and neutral solutions, but dissolves in acids. This behavior illustrates a transition from basic metal-like behavior for bismuth to acidic nonmetallic behavior for antimony.

The hydroxides and oxides of a number of elements considered to be metals by other criteria exhibit both acidic and basic traits. In general the acidity of an oxide or hydroxide of an element increases with the oxidation state of that element. As a consequence the hydroxide of a metal in a low oxidation state will be basic whereas an oxide or hydroxide of the same element in a higher oxidation state may be acidic. For example, chromium(VI) oxide, CrO_3, is strictly an acidic oxide, whereas chromium(II) hydroxide, $Cr(OH)_2$, is a base. Nonmetal oxides and hydroxides are acidic; metals form basic oxides, and hydroxides but may also form acidic ones. The acidity of hydroxides will be discussed in more detail in Section 2–3.

1–4   CONCLUSION

This chapter has illustrated various criteria which can be used to distinguish metals from nonmetals. The properties of the elements change in a gradual fashion and therefore a black and white differentiation is not possible or desirable.

It is important to recognize and remember that the properties of elements and compounds change in a regular fashion related to their position in the periodic table. The changes are in general predictable. Therefore in trying to understand the chemistry of a nonmetal or any element, it is valuable to know its position in the periodic table. Then information about neighboring elements can be combined with a variety of generalizations to give surprisingly accurate information about the element in question. This fact is

Table 1-1
Some Predictions of Mendeleev and Observed
Properties of Germanium

Property	Prediction	Observed
Atomic weight	72	72.59
Color	Dirty gray	Grayish-white
Density	5.5 g/cm^3	5.47 g/cm^3
Product with air	GeO$_2$	GeO$_2$
Reactivity with acids	Slight	None with most
Density of GeO$_2$	4.7 g/cm^3	4.703 g/cm^3
B.p. of GeCl$_4$	100°C	86°C

perhaps best illustrated by comparing the predictions of the properties of germanium made in 1871 by Dmitri Mendeleev, one of the
creators of the modern periodic table, with the actual properties
of the element first isolated fifteen years later in 1886 (Table 1-1).

SUPPLEMENTARY READING LIST

A. F. Wells, *Structural Inorganic Chemistry*, 3rd ed., Clarendon
Press, Oxford, 1962. An excellent presentation of structural
data on the elements and their compounds.
(See Chapter VII for general reading list.)

PROBLEMS

1. You are given a sample of an element. What are three
observations which you could rapidly and easily make which would
suggest whether this element is metallic or nonmetallic?

2. (a) Arrange the following elements in order of increasing
electrical conductivity: Tl, S, Mg, Bi, Si. (b) Arrange the following elements in order of increasing ionization energy: Ga, Te, Ne,

Ba, O. (c) Arrange the following oxides in order of increasing basicity: SeO_2, Sc_2O_3, K_2O, Al_2O_3, As_2O_3.

3. Predict the number of nearest neighbors around each atom of these elements in the solid state: Ca, Mo, P, O, and Ar.

4. Close-packing is found in many substances. Suggest a reason for this fact.

5. Calculate the electronegativities of the noble gases. Assume their electron affinities are zero.

6. Suggested values for the electron affinities of B, C, N, O, and F are 5, 40, 0, 34, and 84 kcal/mole, respectively. Calculate electronegativities of these elements using these values.

7. In a cubic close-packed structure what percent of the space is vacant? (The same percent of space is vacant in the hexagonal close-packed structure.)

8. In a body-centered cubic structure, what percentage of the space is vacant?

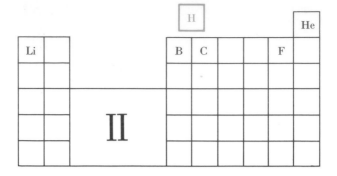

Hydrogen

HYDROGEN forms a huge number of compounds, and these include many which are physiologically and industrially necessary. Moreover, the chemistry of this element is well suited to illustrate the techniques and generalizations which provide a framework for a study of the descriptive chemistry of all elements.

2–1 PERIODIC POSITION OF HYDROGEN

Hydrogen is unique among the elements in that it is not a member of any chemical family; it therefore has no completely satisfactory place in a periodic table. Like the alkali metals hydrogen has a half-filled s subshell and can be ionized to give a singly charged cation. However, it is far easier to remove one electron from an alkali metal; for example, the ionization potential of hydrogen is 313 kcal/mole, whereas that of lithium is 124 kcal/mole. The difficulty in removing the electron from a hydrogen atom can be attributed to the fact that this electron is on the average very near the hydrogen nucleus and thus the electrostatic attraction is great.

Hydrogen can be compared with the halogens in that it accepts an electron to form a hydride ion, H^-. Like the halide ions, the hydride ion has the electronic configuration of a noble gas. However, the electron affinity of hydrogen is much less than that of the halogens.

An analogy can also be drawn between hydrogen and carbon. These elements have similar electronegativities; both have their outer partially filled shell of electrons half-filled; and both form compounds in which the bonding is predominantly covalent. Thus hydrogen, which is not a member of any family of elements, bears resemblances to three families. This diversity of properties makes a study of hydrogen chemistry particularly valuable.

2–2 MOLECULAR HYDROGEN

The element hydrogen exists at room temperature as a di-atomic gaseous molecule, H_2. The forces between two hydrogen molecules are very weak resulting in a boiling point of $-252.8°C$. Gaseous hydrogen is present only in minute quantities in the earth's atmosphere, but the hydrogen atom is probably the pre-dominant species in the universe. Hydrogen is quite abundant on earth in the form of compounds, primarily in H_2O.

Hydrogen has three isotopes, all of which are found in nature. Protium, ^1_1H, containing only a proton in its nucleus is predomi-nant. Deuterium, ^2_1H (also designated D), which contains both a proton and a neutron, makes up 0.015% of the hydrogen on earth, whereas only minute amounts of tritium, ^3_1H, are present ($10^{-15}\%$). Only tritium is radioactive, decaying to give ^3_2He and a β particle (a high-speed electron) (2-1). Its presence on earth results from

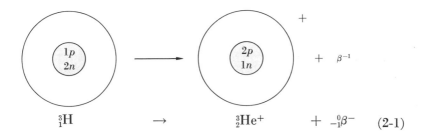

$$^3_1H \qquad \rightarrow \qquad ^3_2He^+ \qquad + \quad _{-1}^0\beta^- \qquad (2\text{-}1)$$

its continuous formation in the upper atmosphere as a result of reaction (2-2). Tritium is being used commercially to produce

$$^{14}_{7}N + ^{1}_{0}n \rightarrow ^{12}_{6}C + ^{3}_{1}H \qquad (2\text{-}2)$$

luminous paints such as those used on watch faces. It is particularly suitable for this purpose since its radioactive decay provides sufficient energy to cause luminescence of the materials in the paint, and yet the potentially dangerous β particles emitted have so little energy that they will not penetrate the glass watch face.

The chemistries of the isotopes of hydrogen are very similar, since nuclear charge and the number of electrons around an atom are primarily responsible for chemical behavior and many physical properties. Since tritium is three times heavier than protium and deuterium is twice as heavy, there are small differences in their properties; frequently reaction rates and equilibria are slightly modified. These differences are called isotope effects, and for most other elements are negligible. One isotope effect is that H^+ is more easily reduced than D^+ (2-3). The separation of protium from

$$\begin{array}{llr} 2H^+ + 2e^- = H_2 & E^0 = & 0.000 \text{ V} \\ 2D^+ + 2e^- = D_2 & E^0 = & -0.0034 \text{ V} \end{array} \qquad (2\text{-}3)$$

deuterium makes use of this fact. The one liter of water remaining after 99,999 liters out of an initial 100,000 liters are electrolyzed is 99.0% D_2O. This separation also results in part from a second isotope effect, namely, that D_3O^+ is reduced at a slower rate than H_3O^+. The melting points of hydrogen and deuterium compounds normally differ slightly; for example, D_2O melts at $3.82°C$ and boils at $101.4°C$. The most striking isotope effects are found in biological systems; in a few cases the replacement of a hydrogen atom by a deuterium completely changes the physiological behavior of a substance. For example, D_2O is toxic to humans.

Preparation

Hydrogen gas has been prepared by a wide variety of reactions. The simplest laboratory methods involve the reaction of certain metals with aqueous acids. The conditions under which hydrogen can be obtained from the reaction of water with a metal can be determined by studying a chart of electrode potentials. Table 2–1 lists a few values of interest and more complete tables are available in a variety of books. Of particular interest is the potential for the conversion of water into hydrogen (2-4). The potential for this reaction depends on the acidity of the solution; in strongly basic

$$2H_2O + 2e^- = H_2 + 2OH^- \qquad E^0 = -0.828 \text{ V} \qquad (2\text{-}4)$$

solution it is about -0.8 V, in neutral solution -0.4 V, and in strongly acidic solution about 0.

As a result, metals which are very good reducing agents, such as sodium, produce hydrogen from basic, neutral, and acidic solution. Less effective reducing agents such as nickel are oxidized by water only in acidic solution. On the basis of data in Table 2–1 one would expect a metal such as aluminum to produce hydrogen readily from basic, neutral, and acidic solution. However in neutral water an oxide coating rapidly forms on the surface of the metal (2-5) which causes further reaction to be immeasurably slow.

$$2Al + 3H_2O \rightarrow Al_2O_3 + 6H_2 \qquad (2\text{-}5)$$

Aluminum does produce hydrogen from both acidic and basic aqueous solutions since under these conditions the oxide coating dissolves or does not form (2-6, 2-7). Zinc exhibits similar behavior.

$$Al_2O_3 + 6H^+ \rightarrow 2Al^{3+} + 3H_2O \qquad (2\text{-}6)$$

$$Al_2O_3 + 3H_2O + 2OH^- \rightarrow 2Al(OH)_4^- \qquad (2\text{-}7)$$

Thus a chart of redox potentials will tell us which metals can be oxidized by water and hence produce hydrogen, but it does not indicate how rapidly the reaction will proceed; in many cases the expected process will not be feasible. The table does indicate that metals such as copper and mercury do not produce hydrogen from water. It should be noted, however, that in some cases the presence of a suitable third substance may cause one of these inactive metals to reduce water to hydrogen (2-8).

$$2Cu + 2H_3O^+ + 2I^- \rightarrow 2CuI + H_2 + 2H_2O \qquad (2\text{-}8)$$

Table 2-1
Electrode Potentials[a]

Half-cell	Standard potential (volts)
$F_2 \quad + 2H^+ + 2e^- = 2HF$	3.06
$FeO_4^{2-} + 8H^+ + 3e^- = Fe^{3+} \quad + 4H_2O$	2.20
$Co^{3+} + \quad e^- = Co^{2+}$	1.808
$MnO_4^- + 8H^+ + 5e^- = Mn^{2+} + 4H_2O$	1.51
$O_2 \quad + 4H^+ + 4e^- = 2H_2O$	1.229
$Hg^{2+} \qquad + 2e^- = Hg$	0.824
$Cu^+ \qquad + \quad e^- = Cu$	0.521
$H^+ \qquad + \quad e^- = \frac{1}{2}H_2$	0.0000
$CuI \qquad + \quad e^- = Cu \quad + I^-$	−0.1852
$Ni^{2+} \qquad + 2e^- = Ni$	−0.250
$Cr^{3+} \qquad + \quad e^- = Cr^{2+}$	−0.408
$H_3PO_3 + 2H^+ + 2e^- = H_3PO_2 + H_2O$	−0.499
$Zn^{2+} \qquad + 2e^- = Zn$	−0.7628
$2H_2O \qquad + 2e^- = H_2 \quad + 2OH^-$	−0.828
$Al^{3+} \qquad + 3e^- = Al$	−1.662
$\frac{1}{2}H_2 \qquad + \quad e^- = H^-$	−2.25
$Na^+ \qquad + \quad e^- = Na$	−2.714

[a] Electrode potentials were taken from A. J. de Bethune and N. A. S. Loud, *Standard Aqueous Electrode Potentials and Temperature Coefficients at 25.0°C.* C. A. Hampel, Skokie, Ill., 1964.

Reducing agents other than metals will also produce hydrogen from water. Hypophosphorous acid (H_3PO_2) is a good reducing agent and is oxidized by water to H_3PO_3. Metal ions such as Cr^{2+} will reduce water; in this case Cr^{3+} and H_2 are formed. The hydride ion is a very powerful reducing agent. Metal hydrides such as NaH react vigorously with H_2O (2-9). Hydride ion also reacts with

$$H^- + H_2O \rightarrow H_2 + OH^- \qquad (2\text{-}9)$$

many other hydrogen containing substances to produce H_2. Compounds such as ammonia and alcohols contain hydrogens which are sufficiently acidic to react with the very strong base H^- (2-10).

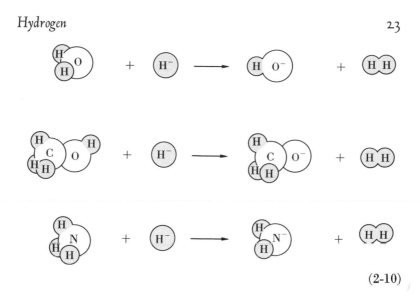

$$(2\text{-}10)$$

The hydrogen preparations suggested here can be conveniently performed in a laboratory, but all involve chemicals which are too expensive for industrial preparations. Commercially, hydrogen is most frequently prepared by one of the following methods. Carbon (in the form of coke) is one of the cheapest reducing agents. It is able to reduce water to hydrogen, but the reaction proceeds at a practical rate only at high temperatures (2-11). The product

$$C + H_2O(g) \rightarrow CO + H_2 \qquad (2\text{-}11)$$

mixture of H_2 and CO is called water gas. Hydrogen is produced in huge quantities as a by-product of the preparation of gasoline from petroleum. One step in this process involves thermal or catalytic cracking of hydrocarbons (2-12). In this reaction a hydrocarbon molecule is fragmented into hydrogen and olefin

$$R—CH_2—CH_2—R' \rightarrow R—CH{=}CH—R' + H_2 \qquad (2\text{-}12)$$

(R and R' represent the remainder of the hydrocarbon)

(R—C=C—R'); the olefins have higher octane[1] values than the

---

[1] The octane value of a gasoline indicates whether the substance will burn smoothly in an internal combustion engine (car motor) or will burn too rapidly (knock).

initial hydrocarbon. A third commercial process is the electrolysis of water to produce H_2 and O_2. This is practical only where electricity is very cheap.

Molecular hydrogen has several uses. Large quantities are consumed in the preparation of oleomargarine. This process is the reverse of reaction (2-12). Double bonds in the readily available liquid oils such as cottonseed oil and corn oil react with hydrogen in the presence of catalysts to give the much more valuable semisolid table spread.

A pound of hydrogen produces a very large amount of heat and lightweight products when reacted with oxidants such as fluorine; therefore it is potentially a very important rocket fuel. The engineering difficulties involved in handling large quantities of this very low boiling substance have somewhat limited this use.

2–3   WATER AND ITS STRUCTURE

Molecular hydrogen has a variety of uses; however, hydrogen compounds are more important. Water is almost certainly the most familiar compound of hydrogen; yet in many ways it is a unique substance. It is the most common solvent and a very convenient one. It is a liquid at normal room temperatures and over a relatively large temperature range. It is nonflammable, nontoxic, and, most important, it dissolves a wide variety of substances. In order to obtain a fundamental understanding of the properties of water, it is necessary to be familiar with its structure.

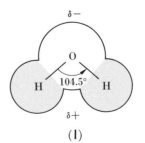

(I)

As a gaseous molecule, water exists in individual units having structure (I). As a result of its bent structure and the fact that oxygen is more electronegative than hydrogen, water molecules are polar. The oxygen end of the molecule has a small negative charge $(\delta -)$; the hydrogen ends, a small positive one $(\delta +)$. We shall see many consequences of this polarity. When a collection of water molecules is cooled, condensation to the liquid occurs; further cooling produces ice. Since the structure of the liquid is more complex than that of the solid, let us next consider the structure of ice.

Ice crystallizes with several distinct structures. We shall consider here only the common form obtained by freezing water at atmospheric pressure; most other forms are stable only at high pressures. From X-ray and neutron diffraction techniques the structure of common ice is now accurately known. X-ray diffraction locates only the oxygen atoms. They are arranged in the fashion depicted in Figure 2–1. Each oxygen has four neighbors at 2.76 A. All O—O O angles are 109.3°, the tetrahedral angle. Recently neutron diffraction studies have found that each hydrogen atom lies directly between two oxygen atoms and is closer to one oxygen (0.97 A) than to the second (1.79 A). In this location the hydrogen reduces the repulsion between the slightly negatively charged oxygens. In fact oxygens separated by a hydrogen in ice are closer together than are neighboring oxygen atoms belonging to two different molecules in other oxygen-containing solids (3.0 A).

A hydrogen in water is bound to the nearest oxygen atom by an essentially covalent interaction. It is attracted weakly to the more distant oxygen by what is known as a *hydrogen bond*. This bond is perhaps best described as resulting from the electrostatic attraction between a slightly positively charged hydrogen in one polar water molecule and a slightly negatively charged oxygen in another. Hydrogen bonding is observed between molecules, one of which contains a hydrogen attached to a very electronegative atom or group and the other having an exposed electronegative atom (Figure 2–2).

Hydrogen bonding has a vital effect on the properties of condensed water and plays an important role in the chemistry of

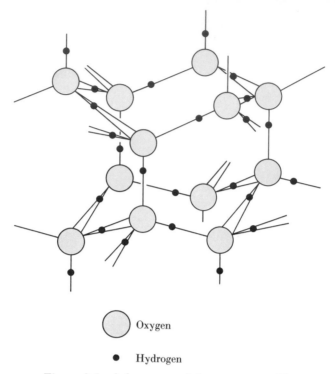

Oxygen

Hydrogen

Figure 2–1   A fragment of the structure of ice.

many hydrogen-containing compounds. The hydrogen bonds which link water molecules to one another in ice are considerably stronger than the van der Waals forces which bind most molecules to one another in the solid and liquid states. They are, however, much weaker than most covalent bonds. (The hydrogen bonds in water have an estimated bond strength of about 4 kcal/mole; the O—H covalent bond in water has a strength of 111 kcal/mole; the van der Waals attraction between two neon atoms is less than 1 kcal/mole.) This results in abnormally high melting and boiling points for water. Neon, a nonhydrogen-bonded substance, contains the same number of electrons as water but boils at −246°C.

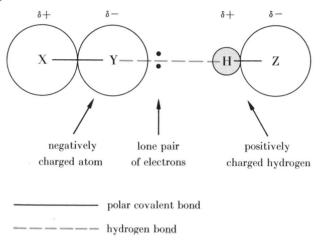

negatively   lone pair   positively
charged atom   of electrons   charged hydrogen

——————————— polar covalent bond

— — — — — — — hydrogen bond

Figure 2-2   A hydrogen bond.

The structure of ice permits the maximum number of hydrogen bonds—one for each hydrogen atom.

The resulting structure is unusual in that it contains considerable empty space (Figure 2-1).   If ice had a structure in which the oxygens were close-packed with hydrogens fitting in holes between the oxygens, the density would be at least 1.9 g/cm³ rather than the 0.917 g/cm³ observed.   The high pressure forms of ice have more compact structures.   When ice melts, it contracts due to the fact that some hydrogen bonds break and a more compact structure results.   Ice is one of very few solids that contracts on melting.   The low density of ice is a vital property, for our climate would certainly be vastly different if ice did not float.

The structure of liquid water has been studied by many scientists; however, complete agreement has not as yet been achieved.   This is due to the fact that liquids in general have largely disordered structures which are hard to describe in terms of a simple model.   Studies have shown that in liquid water each oxygen is on the average near slightly more than four oxygens.   It is generally agreed that a large number of hydrogen bonds are present, and it is clear that there is considerable open space in the structure, even though liquid water is more dense than ice. A simple model which probably resembles liquid water is a structure similar to one of the high-pressure forms of ice. This structure would have some holes in it arising from the loss of some water molecules. The number of holes increases with temperature; this accounts for the fact that the density of water decreases with temperature (above 4°C). At temperatures near 0°C the presence of fragments with a more open ice structure has also been postulated. The breakup of these low-density clusters will then account for the observed increase in density of liquid water as it is warmed from 0 to 4°C.

2-4 REACTIONS OF WATER

Reactions of water can be divided into four classes: Brönsted-Lowry base reactions, Brönsted-Lowry acid reactions, Lewis base reactions, and redox reactions.

Water as a Brönsted-Lowry Base

One of the most important and familiar reactions of water is its interaction with acids to produce hydrated hydrogen ions. In this reaction water functions as a *Brönsted-Lowry base, a hydrogen ion acceptor*. With strong acids this reaction goes to completion (2-13). However, water is not a strong enough base to remove

$$HX + H_2O \rightarrow H_3O^+ + X^- \qquad (2\text{-}13)$$

H^+ from every molecule of weak acids, such as HF (2-14). Stronger bases may cause the complete dissociation of this acid; for example,

$$HF + H_2O \rightleftharpoons H_3O^+ + F^- \qquad (2\text{-}14)$$

HF dissolves in liquid ammonia and dissociates completely (2-15);

$$HF + NH_3 \rightarrow NH_4^+ + F^- \qquad (2\text{-}15)$$

in this solvent HF behaves as a strong acid.

The acidity of binary hydrides (compounds with the formula H_xY_y) in water is a periodic property. The acidity of the hydrogen halides decreases in the order HI > HBr > HCl > HF. The hydrogen halides other than HF are strong acids in aqueous solution. In the series of hydrides HF, H_2O, NH_3, and CH_4, only HF is appreciably acidic. Water is a very weak acid and NH_3 is weaker, giving up H^+ only to very strong bases such as hydride ion H^-. The acidic properties of methane CH_4 are so slight that they are usually neglected.

The acidity in water of the other important class of acids, oxyacids, can be predicted with surprising accuracy in a simple way. Oxyacids contain a central element X to which are attached oxygen atoms. Acidic hydrogens are attached to these oxygen atoms. A general formula for these acids is $XO_m(OH)_n$; for example, sulfuric acid (H_2SO_4) and boric acid (H_3BO_3) are oxyacids and can be written as $SO_2(OH)_2$ and $B(OH)_3$; the latter formulas better represent the structures of the pure compounds (II, III). The acidity of these acids has been observed to be related to the value of m. The strongest common oxyacid, perchloric acid ($HClO_4$ or ClO_3OH), has $m = 3$. Very weak oxyacids such as boric ($B(OH)_3$) and hypochlorous ($ClOH$) acids have $m = 0$. Table 2–2 gives a more quantitative relationship between the equilibrium constant for the dissociation of the acid and the value of m. The negative values of $\log K$ given for strong acids have little significance in water. However, in solvents such as pure H_2SO_4 it has been possible to show that $HClO_4$ is a stronger acid than H_2SO_4 or HNO_3.

To complete this discussion of the acidities of oxyacids let us consider acids containing more than one acidic hydrogen. Phosphoric acid, $PO(OH)_3$, has three. Using the generalizations in

(II)   (III)

Table 2-2

Acid Dissociation Constants for Oxyacids

$$XO_m(OH)_n \underset{H_2O}{\overset{K}{\rightleftharpoons}} XO_{m+1}(OH)_{n-1}^- + H_3O^+$$

$$K = \frac{[H_3O^+][XO_{m+1}(OH)_{n-1}^-]}{[XO_m(OH)_n]}$$

Acid	m	Predicted[a] $-\log K$	Observed $-\log K$
HClO$_4$	3	-7	Very large neg. value
H$_2$SO$_4$	2	-2	Large neg. value
HNO$_3$	2	-2	Large neg. value
H$_3$PO$_4$	1	3	2.12
H$_2$SO$_3$	1	3	1.90
HClO$_2$	1	3	1.94
HNO$_2$	1	3	3.3
H$_5$IO$_6$	1	3	3.29
H$_3$BO$_3$	0	8	9.22
H$_6$TeO$_6$	0	8	8.80
HClO	0	8	7.50

[a] $-\log K$ changes by about $+5$ when m decreases by 1.

Table 2-2, we can predict that the equilibrium constant for the loss of one H$^+$ will be 10^{-3}. The second H$^+$ to leave would be departing from an anion with a charge of -1. Reaction (2-16) would therefore be electrostatically more difficult. The loss of

$$H_2PO_4^- \overset{H_2O}{\rightleftharpoons} HPO_4^{2-} + H_3O^+ \qquad (2\text{-}16)$$

H$^+$ from HPO$_4^{2-}$ should be even less favorable. Experiments have demonstrated that in oxyacids $(XO_m(OH)_n)$ containing only one X per molecule the K for acid dissociation decreases by about 10^5 for each H$^+$ lost. Therefore the K's for phosphoric acid could be anticipated to be 10^{-3}, 10^{-8}, and 10^{-13}; experimental values are about 10^{-2}, 10^{-7}, and 10^{-12}. A more complete discussion of the acidity of binary and oxyacids can be found in references listed at the end of the chapter.

Since the simple rules for predicting and remembering the acidities of oxyacids work well, it is worthwhile to consider reasons for their success. A relatively simple explanation can be proposed in terms of the electrostatic attraction of H^+ ion and an oxygen on the anion formed when the acid dissociates, for example, the attraction of H^+ for an oxygen in ClO_4^- ion. The greater this attraction, the weaker is the acid. Since chlorine and oxygen have about the same electronegativity, one can claim that the -1 charge of ClO_4^- is distributed equally between these atoms; thus the charge on each oxygen is $-\frac{1}{5}$ and the H^+ is attracted by this charge.

It is more difficult to assign a charge to the oxygens in the HSO_4^- ion so that the acidities of $HClO_4$ and H_2SO_4 can be compared. A simple approach involves the assumptions that the negative charge on the ion is equally distributed among the oxygens and the sulfur, and that the H in HSO_4^- is an H^+; this will result in a -2 charge being distributed over the other five atoms.[2] On the basis of this charge distribution each oxygen bears a $-\frac{2}{5}$ charge and hence H_2SO_4 should be a weaker acid than $HClO_4$. A similar analysis for H_3PO_4 predicts a $-\frac{3}{5}$ charge on each oxygen and hence is in line with its observed acidity.

Water as a Brönsted-Lowry Acid

Water not only accepts H^+ from acids, but also donates H^+ to suitable bases. (*Brönsted-Lowry acids* are defined as *donors of H^+.*) The most familiar example is the reaction of ammonia with water (2-17). Other familiar bases which accept protons from water are the acetate and phosphate ions (2-18, 2-19). The ability of some molecules or ions to remove a proton from water (their basicity) can be predicted using the rules previously described for acidity. The products NH_4^+, CH_3CO_2H, and HPO_4^{2-} formed in reactions 2-17–2-19 are all acids. Weak bases produce relatively strong acids on reaction with water; strong bases produce weak

---

[2] It is informative to try more refined assumptions and to see whether they lead to accurate predictions of acidity; for example, fractional charges may be distributed on the basis of the relative electronegativities of the atoms (see Problem 12 at the end of this chapter).

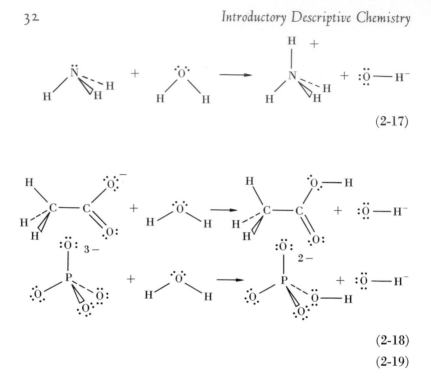

(2-17)

(2-18)
(2-19)

acids.   Since CH_3CO_2H is the strongest of the three acids, $CH_3CO_2^-$ is the weakest base.   The HPO_4^{2-} ion is the weakest of the three acids and hence PO_4^{3-} is the strongest of these bases.

Water as a Lewis Base

Water in the Brönsted-Lowry sense is both an acid and a base; many reactions of this molecule depend upon its properties as a Lewis base.   (A *Lewis base* is defined as an *electron pair donor; a Lewis acid* is defined as an *electron pair acceptor*.)   The simplest example of this type of reaction is the formation of molecules such as H_2OBF_3 (2-20), which is formed when equal amounts of gaseous BF_3 and H_2O are mixed.   Water provides the electron pair in the covalent bond which is the primary link between boron and oxygen in this molecule.

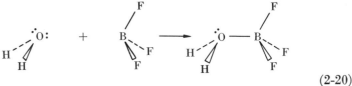

$$(2\text{-}20)$$

The most common species in which water can be considered to be functioning as a Lewis base are hydrated metal ions (IV). It is clear that water molecules interact strongly with dissolved ions. If this were not so, salts would not dissolve in water, since it is known that the forces binding ions together in solids are quite large. The water-ion interactions in most cases can be considered as primarily an electrostatic attraction between the charged ion and the oppositely charged end of the polar water molecule (V). The interaction between water molecules and metal ions with charges of two or greater is sufficiently large that these ions carry water molecules with them as they move about in solution. Molecules directly next to a metal ion are said to be in its *coordination sphere*. In many cases it has been observed that there are six water

(IV)

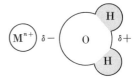 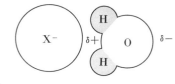

(V)

molecules in the coordination sphere, but certainly the number of such water molecules depends on the charge and size of the metal ion as well perhaps as other factors. It is believed that most singly charged cations and essentially all anions bind water molecules too weakly to actually carry them along as the ion moves in solution.

A particularly important hydrated ion is the hydrogen ion. The bare proton is known independently only in the gas phase. In condensed phases it is always associated with other atoms. In water abundant evidence suggests strong association with one water to give H_3O^+ (VI); this ion in turn is certainly hydrated. A $H_3O^+(H_2O)_3$ species has been postulated and is consistent with data from certain types of experiments. The positive ion-oxygen attraction is probably primarily electrostatic in hydrated ions, but the use of the basically covalent Lewis acid base adduct concept to describe these species is helpful.

Reactions in which a water molecule displaces another group from a molecule or ion can be visualized as the replacement of one Lewis base by another (2-21, 2-22). This type of reaction is frequently called *hydrolysis* or *aquation* and is important in both organic and inorganic systems.

Redox Reactions of Water

A fourth class of reactions of water involves its oxidation and reduction. Water functions as both an oxidizing and reducing agent, and as a result neither very strong oxidizing nor strong reducing agents can exist in water. As previously noted (Section 2-2) Cr^{2+}, H_3PO_2, H^-, and other strong reducing agents are oxidized by water with the production of H_2. In contrast, strong

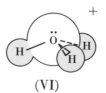

(VI)

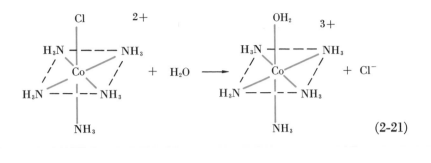

(2-21)

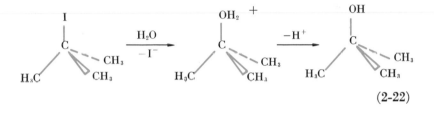

(2-22)

oxidizing agents such as F_2, FeO_4^{2-}, and hydrated Co^{3+} oxidize water to O_2. Equation 2-23 gives the half-cell reaction for the

$$O_2 + 4e^- + 4H^+ = 2H_2O \qquad E^0 = 1.229 \text{ V} \qquad (2\text{-}23)$$

oxidation of water and its potential; the potential is pH-dependent, being 0.815 V at pH = 7.0 and 0.401 V at pH = 14.0. Therefore, in acidic aqueous solutions oxidizing agents with potentials greater than 1.23 V and reducing agents with potentials more negative than 0.00 V (see Section 2–2) are unstable. Some of the common strong oxidizing agents, such as MnO_4^- and Ce^{4+}, have potentials greater than 1.23 V and will oxidize water to O_2. Fortunately, however, these reactions are very slow, and solutions of these ions can be stored for months without noticeable reaction if suitable precautions are taken. The use of redox potential tables allows one to determine which ions will be stable with respect to redox reactions in water, but there are many examples of ions that are potentially able to oxidize water but do so only at a very slow rate.

2–5 OTHER NONMETAL HYDRIDES[3]

Hydrogen fluoride and ammonia are common and useful compounds. Both are gases at room temperature but their boiling points (19°C and −33°C) are unusually high for compounds with such small molecular weights. This property, which they share with water, results from the presence of strong hydrogen bonds which hold neighboring molecules together. Hydrogen bonding in general is found among polar molecules which contain an unshared pair of electrons and hydrogens which have a considerable positive charge. Because fluorine, oxygen, and nitrogen are very electronegative, the hydrogens in HF, H_2O, and NH_3 bear a considerable positive charge; the polarity of these molecules arises because of their shape and the presence of polar bonds. The large polarity of these molecules makes them excellent solvents for many salts and other substances. The use of HF and NH_3 as solvents is limited, however, since they are liquids only below normal room temperature. To further complicate its use, HF attacks glass containers and is an excellent solvent for skin.

Liquid ammonia is less rapidly reduced than water and therefore stronger reducing agents can be used in it. Alkali metals dissolve in ammonia to give dilute solutions which are blue and concentrated solutions which have a copper-like color. There is convincing evidence which indicates that the blue solutions contain alkali metal ions and solvated electrons (2-24). The solvated electrons are responsible for the blue color. Since the electron is a

$$Na \xrightarrow{NH_3(l)} Na(NH_3)_x{}^+ + e(NH_3)_y{}^- \qquad (2\text{-}24)$$

very powerful reducing agent, solutions of alkali metals in ammonia (and other amines) are excellent reagent-solvent systems for difficult reductions. In the presence of moisture or catalysts such as transition metal salts these solutions decompose and yield H_2 and $NaNH_2$.

---

[3] The use of the term hydride need not imply that the compound contains H^- ion.

Methane, CH_4, is the simplest hydride of carbon. It is a nonpolar molecule and boils at $-162°C$; therefore it is not very similar to NH_3, H_2O, and HF. The chemistry of methane and the many other carbon hydrogen compounds is of vital importance, but the interested reader should consult a text on organic chemistry.

The boron hydrides are an unusual group of compounds which have a variety of novel structures. Their properties will be discussed in Chapter III.

The hydrides of the heavier nonmetals are gases at room temperature and are less stable than the hydrides of the light nonmetals. The stability of the hydrides of a family of elements decreases regularly as the mass of the central element increases; for example, ammonia is the most stable hydride of the group V elements; BiH_3 is the least stable. Only trace amounts of PbH_4 and BiH_3 have been detected, and H_2Te and HI are readily decomposed to hydrogen and the nonmetal. Another general feature of the hydrides of the heavy nonmetals is their toxicity. Arsine (AsH_3) and phosphine (PH_3) are very poisonous gases, and H_2S, which is widely and carelessly used in undergraduate laboratories, is a poison of toxicity comparable to hydrogen cyanide. It is thus fortunate that H_2S has such a strong odor that one can detect minute quantities of this gas.

A property of nonmetal hydrides that is shared by few other classes of compounds is catenation. *Catenation* means the formation of chains of identical atoms. Carbon in hydrocarbons (CH_3—CH_3, $CH_3CH_2CH_3$, etc.) displays this property to a remarkable extent. Silicon, germanium, and tin, the next heavier elements in the carbon family, also exhibit catenation but silicon chains longer than Si_6 and germanium chains longer than Ge_8 have not been isolated; however, evidence for longer chains of both silicon and germanium has been presented. Tin forms Sn_2H_6, but this compound decomposes when warmed to room temperature. Nitrogen, phosphorus, and oxygen form hydrazine (N_2H_4), diphosphine (P_2H_4), and hydrogen peroxide (H_2O_2), respectively; recently the existence of H_2O_3 has also been reported. Sulfur is the only other element to form catenated hydrides. Sulfanes (hydrogen polysulfides) with the stoichiometries H_2S_2 to H_2S_6 have been prepared, and mixtures of higher sulfanes have been reported. These and the other catenated hydrogen compounds except those of carbon are quite reactive.

2–6   HYDROGEN COMPOUNDS OF METALS

Hydrogen compounds of metals are in general relatively unstable and reactive. The stability of binary hydrides is a periodic property, decreasing for elements toward the left and bottom of the periodic table; in other words, as the metallic character of the element increases, the stability of the hydrogen compound generally decreases. Although the metal-hydrogen compounds are relatively unstable, many have been prepared and studied. In some of these metal hydrides good evidence for the presence of hydride (H^-) ions has been presented and thus they are called "ionic" hydrides. The remaining metal hydrides show a diversity of properties; a few of these compounds will be described to illustrate their behavior.

Evidence for the ionic nature of the hydrides of the alkali metals and of Ca^{2+}, Sr^{2+}, and Ba^{2+} comes from the observation that they are good conductors of electricity near and above their melting points. Since hydrogen is not very electronegative the bonding in these compounds must also have considerable covalent character. The presence of H^- in the ionic hydrides is suggested by their behavior on electrolysis. Electrolysis of molten LiH or of solutions of the other hydrides in liquid low melting salts yields hydrogen at the anode, which indicates that hydrogen is produced by oxidation of H^-. Electrolysis cannot be performed in water since water reacts vigorously with these compounds to yield hydrogen and a solution of the metal hydroxides. Additional evidence for the presence of H^- is the crystalline structure of these compounds. For example, neutron and X-ray diffraction studies show that the alkali metal hydrides have the rock salt(NaCl) structure (Figure 2–3). The hydride ions occupy the sites occupied by chloride ions in NaCl crystals.

The ionic hydrides are colorless, crystalline, very reactive substances. Their reactivity arises from the presence of the H^- ion,

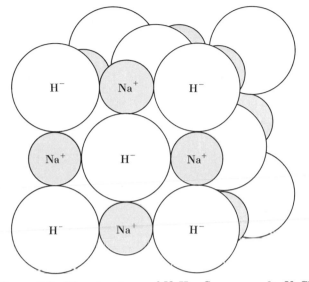

Figure 2–3   The structure of NaH.   Common salt, NaCl, also has this structure.

which is both a powerful base and a powerful reducing agent. Therefore substances possessing hydrogens which are at all acidic (for example, ammonia) will react to give hydrogen, and materials with any oxidizing ability will be reduced.

Lithium hydride is unusual in that it reacts much less rapidly than other ionic hydrides and is sufficiently stable to be melted without decomposition.   (Its melting point is 680°C.)   This surprising behavior can be rationalized by noting that LiH is the closest analog of the very stable H_2 molecule.

Since the remaining metal-hydrogen compounds do not exhibit a common set of properties, let us consider a few compounds which illustrate their diverse behavior.   Beryllium and magnesium hydrides have been prepared and have properties, such as reactivity with water and reducing ability, in common with the ionic hydrides.   Like the ionic hydrides they are more dense than the parent metals.   They are structurally somewhat different from the ionic hydrides, and covalent bonding is certainly more important.

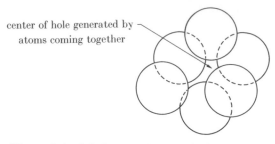

center of hole generated by
atoms coming together

Figure 2–4   A hole in a close-packed structure.

It has been suggested that the bonding and structure of BeH_2 may resemble that of the boron hydrides (see Chapter III).

Uranium hydride, UH_3, is a black pyrophoric[4] substance.

$$2U + 3H_2 \underset{450°C}{\overset{250°C}{\rightleftarrows}} 2UH_3 \qquad (2\text{-}25)$$

It is formed by the reversible reaction of the metal with H_2 (2-25). This reaction has been used for the preparation of pure hydrogen. The compound is unlike ionic hydrides in color, in that it is less dense than the pure metal, and in that it conducts electricity like a metal.   Delocalized covalent or metallic interactions must be largely responsible for the properties of this compound.   Like ionic hydrides and like the uranium and hydrogen from which it is prepared, UH_3 is a powerful reducing agent.

Titanium hydride is similar to several transition metal hydrides.   Its common stoichiometry is about $TiH_{1.7}$, but samples with hydrogen titanium ratios up to 2.00 can be prepared.   This and other transition metal hydrides are *interstitial compounds*. These substances have structures similar to that of the larger element present; the smaller element (in this case, hydrogen) fills holes between the regular lattice sites (Figure 2–4).   It is common for interstitial compounds to exist over a range of stoichiometries; the samples differ only in the number of holes which are occupied.

Titanium hydride looks like a metal and has metallic conductivity.   Evidence has been presented which suggests that both

---

[4] Pyrophoric substances ignite when exposed to air.

hydrogen and titanium have a positive charge in titanium hydride. It has been proposed that this and similar compounds can be viewed as alloys of hydrogen and the metal. In these alloys, hydrogen exists as H^+, with its electron delocalized over the entire structure. Alternatives to the alloy hypothesis have also been presented.

Titanium "adsorbs" 1600 times its own volume of hydrogen gas in forming $TiH_{1.7}$. In fact, hydrogen atoms are more densely packed in $TiH_{1.7}$ than in liquid hydrogen. Titanium hydride is less dense than the pure metal; the presence of hydrogen swells the normal titanium lattice. Titanium hydride is stable in air but is a strong reducing agent and is used commercially as such.

Palladium metal will adsorb 900 times its volume of hydrogen. The amount of hydrogen adsorbed increases when the metal is finely divided and decreases when the metal is heated. Adsorbtion of hydrogen expands the palladium metal lattice and decreases the metallic conductivity. Palladium hydrides have stoichiometries with hydrogen-palladium ratios up to about 0.6. The ability of uranium, palladium, titanium, and other metals to adsorb hydrogen reversibly led early workers to consider the hydrogen as physically adsorbed (this implies that no chemical bonds are formed). Most hydrides of this type are now considered to be true compounds, since their formation produces a moderate amount of heat and they tend to at least approach a definite structure.

The interaction of palladium with hydrogen has many uses. This metal is a very effective catalyst for the introduction of hydrogen into organic compounds, a property which is attributed to the dissociation of hydrogen molecules into atoms at the metal surface. Palladium has also been used to prepare pure hydrogen, since hydrogen passes through palladium metal whereas other gases cannot. This unusual transport of a gas through a metal seems to be due to the formation of hydrogen atoms at the metal surface and their movement through the metal.

2–7   PREPARATION OF HYDRIDES

Hydrogen compounds of most elements can be prepared by direct reaction between the elements. This is certainly the most

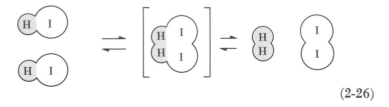

$$\text{(2-26)}$$

general mode of preparation and is equally effective for metals and nonmetals.

The mechanisms for reactions of several nonmetals with hydrogen have been studied. Iodine reacts with hydrogen at room temperature by a simple collision process (2-26). The mechanisms of the reactions of the other halogens with hydrogen involve *free radicals*.[5] The steps in the mechanism for the reaction of hydrogen and bromine are outlined in equations 2-27–2-31. The step in

$$Br_2 \rightarrow \quad 2\ Br\cdot \qquad \text{(2-27)}$$

$$Br\cdot + H_2 \quad \rightarrow HBr + H\cdot \qquad \text{(2-28)}$$

$$H\cdot + Br_2 \quad \rightarrow HBr + Br\cdot \qquad \text{(2-29)}$$

$$H\cdot + HBr \rightarrow H_2 \quad + Br\cdot \qquad \text{(2-30)}$$

$$Br\cdot + Br\cdot \xrightarrow{D} Br_2 \qquad \text{(2-31)}$$

which atoms react with each other (2-31) must occur in the presence of a third body (D) which absorbs some of the energy produced in the reaction. In its absence the molecule formed has sufficient energy to redissociate. The third body may be a wall of the reaction vessel or any gas molecule.

Chlorine and flourine react by similar but not identical mechanisms which involve radicals. At high temperatures a mechanism involving radicals also contributes to the hydrogen-iodine reaction. It is informative to seek an explanation for the observation that iodine is the only halogen to react with hydrogen by a simple collision process. This observation tells us that the radical process

---

[5] A free radical is an atom or molecule which has unpaired s or p electrons.

Hydrogen 43

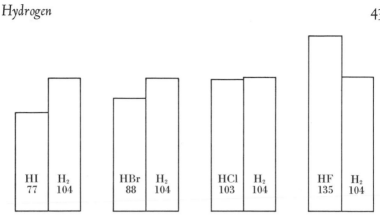

Figure 2–5 The bond energies of hydrogen and the hydrogen halides (kcal/mole).

for the formation of HI is so much slower than the collision process at low temperatures that it is not observed. The radical mechanism provides the faster path for the other halogens both at room temperature and higher temperatures.

It is thought that the reason a radical mechanism is observed only at high temperatures in the hydrogen-iodine reaction is the unfavorable energy change in reaction 2-32. Since the HI bond is considerably weaker than the H_2 bond, this reaction should be

$$I\cdot + H_2 \rightleftharpoons HI + H\cdot \qquad (2\text{-}32)$$

quite endothermic. It is probable therefore that the equilibrium will be quite unfavorable and the forward reaction rate will be slow. Figure 2–5 shows the relative bond strengths of the hydrogen halides and hydrogen. These data suggest that reactions in which H—H bonds are directly converted into H—X bonds should occur most readily when X is flourine and least readily when X is iodine.

The reaction between hydrogen and oxygen has been carefully studied. Mixtures of these two gases do not react during extended periods of time at room temperature, unless the reaction is initiated by a flame or in some other manner. The reason for the failure to react is that either hydrogen or oxygen molecules must be dissociated into atoms to start the reaction; a gas at room temperature is unlikely to concentrate enough energy in one gas molecule to dissociate such a firmly bonded species. The mechanism which has been proposed for the reaction involves initiation by dissociation of H_2 into $H\cdot$ atoms. A relatively complicated radical chain reaction follows which produces $HO_2\cdot$ and $HO\cdot$ radicals and ultimately H_2O. All of the processes involving radicals described here are chain reactions. Once they are initiated they frequently proceed with explosive rapidity.

The formation of ammonia by direct combination of nitrogen and hydrogen (Haber process) proceeds at a reasonable rate at temperatures above 400°C and then only in the presence of catalysts. The slowness of the reaction must be related to the difficulty in breaking the strong bonds which unite the atoms in the nitrogen molecule ($:N{\equiv}N:$).

Gaseous hydrides are often produced by the reaction of binary salts with water or an acid. The reaction with water is feasible when the binary salt is derived from a very weak acid. A convenient synthesis of ND_3 illustrates this procedure (2-33). (Mg_3N_2 can be considered the salt of $Mg(OH)_2$ and the very weak "acid"

$$Mg_3N_2 + 6D_2O \rightarrow 3Mg(OD)_2 + 2ND_3 \uparrow \qquad (2\text{-}33)$$

NH_3; in fact, NH_3 does not act as an acid at all in water.)

A more common procedure is the reaction of a salt with a strong nonvolatile acid. Since sulfuric acid is inexpensive, it is frequently used (2-34, 2-35). The product hydrides are volatile,

$$CaF_2 + H_2SO_4(\text{conc}) \rightarrow CaSO_4 \quad + 2HF \uparrow \qquad (2\text{-}34)$$

$$NaCl + H_2SO_4(\text{conc}) \rightarrow NaHSO_4 + HCl \uparrow \qquad (2\text{-}35)$$

escape, and can be collected in pure form. Concentrated sulfuric acid cannot be used when the salt is readily oxidized. For example, HBr and HI are not prepared in this way because bromide and iodide ions yield bromine, iodine, and other oxidation products on reaction with concentrated sulfuric acid. Phosphoric acid is not a strong oxidizing agent but is nonvolatile and can be used in place of H_2SO_4.

When product purity is not important, volatile acids can be

reacted with salts. A common laboratory preparation of H_2S uses hydrochloric acid (2-36). The gaseous H_2S produced will be con-

$$FeS + HCl(\text{aqueous}) \rightarrow Fe^{2+} + 2Cl^- + H_2S \uparrow \quad (2\text{-}36)$$

taminated with water and HCl vapors.

The ionic metal hydrides and $LiAlH_4$ (lithium tetrahydrido-aluminate(III)) and $NaBH_4$ (sodium tetrahydridoborate(III)) have been widely used in recent years to prepare hydrogen compounds, particularly those which are reactive or unstable. The use of these compounds has markedly increased the rate of progress in the study of the hydride chemistry of boron, silicon, germanium, and other semimetallic elements. Examples of preparations of inorganic hydrides that have been made possible or simplified by the use of these compounds are presented in reactions 2-37–2-39.

$$AlCl_3 + \quad 4LiH \rightarrow LiAlH_4 + 3LiCl \quad (2\text{-}37)$$

$$SnCl_4 + LiAlH_4 \rightarrow SnH_4 \quad + LiCl \quad + AlCl_3 \quad (2\text{-}38)$$

$$Si_3Cl_8 + 2LiAlH_4 \rightarrow Si_3H_8 \quad + 2LiCl + 2AlCl_3 \quad (2\text{-}39)$$

These reactions are almost always performed in anhydrous solvents such as ether; the procedures in general also give side reactions so that the equations imply only major products.

SUPPLEMENTARY READING LIST

R. T. Sanderson, "Principles of Hydrogen Chemistry," *J. Chem. Ed.*, **41**, 331 (1964). A summary of important features of the chemical behavior of hydrogen.

R. P. Bell, *The Proton in Chemistry*, Cornell University Press, Ithaca, 1959. A description of the behavior of hydrogen ions in solutions and of acid-base behavior.

G. C. Pimentel and A. L. McClellen, *The Hydrogen Bond*, Freeman, San Francisco, 1960.

G. Liebowitz, *The Solid-State Chemistry of Binary Metal Hydrides*, Benjamin, New York, 1965.

Thomas R. P. Gibb, Jr., "Primary Solid Hydrides" *in* F. A. Cotton (ed.), _Progress in Inorganic Chemistry_, Vol. III, pp. 315–509, Wiley (Interscience), New York, 1962.

Bernard Siegel, "Hydride Formation by Atomic Hydrogen Reactions," _J. Chem. Ed._, **38**, 496 (1961).

J. O. Edwards, _Inorganic Reaction Mechanisms: An Introduction_, Benjamin, New York, 1964. A presentation of a variety of mechanistic data on inorganic reactions.

(See Chapter VII for a general reading list.)

PROBLEMS

_1._ An element reacts with hydrogen. The product is a gas at room temperature. Is this product when liquified likely to be an electrical conductor? Why?

_2._ Suggest methods for distinguishing between these compounds: (a) H_2 and D_2; (b) H_2O and NH_3; (c) H_3BO_3 and H_2SO_4; (d) LiH and $TiH_{1.7}$.

_3._ Arrange these species in order of increasing Brönsted-Lowry acidity: H_3O^+, ClO_4^-, NH_2^-, HCl, HNO_2, H_2O, $HClO_4$, OH^-, $H_2PO_4^-$.

_4._ Metal hydrides are convenient portable sources of gaseous hydrogen. How many grams of hydrogen can be prepared from the reaction of 20.0 g of MgH_2 with an excess of water? What volume of hydrogen gas would be produced if the gas were collected over water at 25.0°C at an atmospheric pressure of 740 mm of Hg? The vapor pressure of water at 25.0°C is 23.8 mm of Hg.

_5._ $$2H_2 + O_2 \rightarrow 2H_2O$$

This chemical reaction can be considered the sum of which two electrochemical half-cells? What is the standard potential of this reaction?

6. Complete and balance these chemical equations:

$$
\begin{array}{ll}
\text{NaBr} & + \text{H}_3\text{PO}_4 \rightarrow \\
\text{LiAlH}_4 & + \text{H}_2\text{O} \quad \rightarrow \\
\text{Cu} & + \text{H}^+ \xrightarrow{\text{H}_2\text{O}} \\
\text{NaH} & + \text{NH}_3 \quad \rightarrow \\
\text{HCl} & + \text{H}_2\text{O} \quad \rightarrow \\
\text{NaH}_2\text{PO}_4 & + \text{H}_2\text{O} \quad \rightarrow \\
\text{Na}_2\text{SO}_4 & + \text{H}_2\text{O} \quad \rightarrow \\
\text{AlCl}_3 & + \text{H}_2\text{O} \quad \rightarrow \\
& \qquad\qquad \rightarrow \text{ZrH}_{1.9} \\
& \qquad\qquad \rightarrow \text{H}_2\text{SO}_4
\end{array}
$$

7. Suggest explanations for these observations. (a) H_2 boils at $-257.7°C$. (b) Light molecules are very weakly held by the earth's gravity but hydrogen is abundant on earth. (c) The heat of formation of H_2O is greater than that of H_2S. (d) The H_3 molecule has not been isolated. (e) The melting point of LiH is much greater than that of CH_4. (f) Water is a stronger oxidizing agent in acid than in basic solution.

8. Free radical processes include three types of steps: initiation reactions, chain-propagating reactions, and chain-terminating reactions. Classify reactions 2-27–2-31 into these three groups.

9. Present an explanation for the observation that the electron affinity of hydrogen is much less than that of fluorine.

10. Make an estimate of the density that ice would have, if the oxygen atoms were close-packed.

11. Which elements are sufficiently good reducing agents to liberate hydrogen gas from acidic aqueous solution? Place the information collected on a periodic table format and see whether reducing ability is a periodic property. Handbooks of chemistry contain redox potential tables which include most elements.

12. (a) Estimate the charge on the oxygen atoms of $HClO_4$, H_2SO_4, and H_3PO_4. Assume that for each 0.1 difference in electronegativity between bonded atoms a charge separation of 0.04 is introduced. For example the electronegativities of the atoms in HNO_3 are H (2.10), N (3.07), and O (3.50). The differences in charge between neighboring atoms are therefore N—O (3.50–3.07) (0.04) = 0.17 and O—H (3.50–2.10)(0.04) = 0.56. The distribution of charge most consistent with these charge separations and the over-all neutrality of the molecule is H (+0.43), N (+0.02), and each O (−0.15). (b) On the basis of the calculated charges on O predict the relative acidities of $HClO_4$, H_2SO_4, H_3PO_4, and HNO_3. This procedure gives results which are relatively consistent for both charged and uncharged oxyacids.

Be			B	C			
			Al	Si			
		III					

Boron Hydrides

BORON IS IN MANY WAYS a unique element. Its chemistry is surprisingly different from that of aluminum, the next heavier element in its family, and it is not particularly similar to its other neighbors beryllium and carbon. A particularly unusual class of boron compounds is its hydrides. The structures of these compounds are unlike those of any other compounds and the existing bonding theories had to be extended or modified to account for their properties. Before considering the chemistry of the boron hydrides it is useful to learn a little about the properties of boron and its compounds.

Boron is a dark, very hard, high-melting, semiconducting solid. Aluminum in contrast is a silver-white, soft, relatively low-melting solid, and is a good conductor of electricity. Elemental boron is chemically quite unreactive; even when it is finely divided it is dissolved only very slowly by hot concentrated oxidizing acids. Aluminum dissolves rapidly in dilute acids to give hydrated Al^{3+} ions. Positive aqueous ions of boron have not been observed. Boric acid $(B(OH)_3)$ functions only as a weak acid; it does not dissociate to give hydroxide ions. Aluminum hydroxide, $Al(OH)_3$, is amphoteric but acts primarily as a base.

49

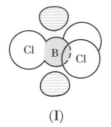

(I)

The principal similarities between boron and aluminum chemistry are the stoichiometry of their compounds and the fact that compounds such as the trihalides function as Lewis acids (3-1).

$$: NH_3 + BCl_3 \rightarrow H_3N : BCl_3 \qquad (3\text{-}1)$$

The similarity in the stoichiometry of their compounds is to be expected since both elements have three electrons beyond a noble gas core; thus boron and aluminum in their compounds exhibit an apparent oxidation state of $+3$. Compounds of both elements frequently function as Lewis acids, since in many derivatives (such as the trihalides) only three of the four low-energy s and p orbitals are used in bonding and one empty orbital is available (I).

Boron resembles silicon in several respects; these two elements are one of the best examples of *diagonal periodic relationships*. Elements such as lithium and magnesium, beryllium and aluminum, and boron and silicon, which lie on diagonals on the periodic table, have many similar properties. The most marked resemblance between silicon and boron is in the acid-base character of their oxides and hydroxides. Both oxides and hydroxides are weakly acidic, as is demonstrated by their reactivity with bases. Neither reacts with H^+ and hence they are not basic. The similar acidities of $B(OH)_3$ and $Si(OH)_4$ are consistent with the generalization on the acidity of oxyacids presented in Table 2-2. The similarities noted for elements on diagonals on the periodic table has been attributed to the fact that the ratio of the charge on the atom (when it has lost its valence electrons) to the radius of this ion is relatively constant along the diagonal. For example, the charges on boron and silicon after the loss of their

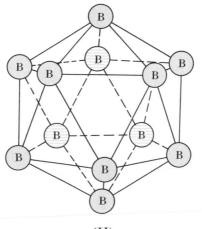

(II)

valence electrons are +3 and +4. The radii of B^{3+} and Si^{4+} are 0.20 and 0.39. The charge-radius ratios are 15 and 10. The charge-radius ratio is known to reflect the properties of an element and particularly the acidity of its oxide and hydroxide (the greater the charge-radius ratio, the greater the acidity of the oxide or hydroxide).

Several crystalline modifications of elemental boron have been observed; the structures of the three which have been determined contain icosahedral B_{12} units (II). Boron is the only element with this type of structure, one intermediate between that of close-packed metals and the molecular arrangements of many non-metals. The icosahedral arrangement or fragments thereof is found in many boron hydrides.

3–2 BORON HYDRIDES

The pioneering work in the field of boron hydride chemistry was done by Alfred Stock, a German scientist and professor, and his students between 1912 and 1936. These scientists developed both the equipment and techniques necessary to handle these vola-

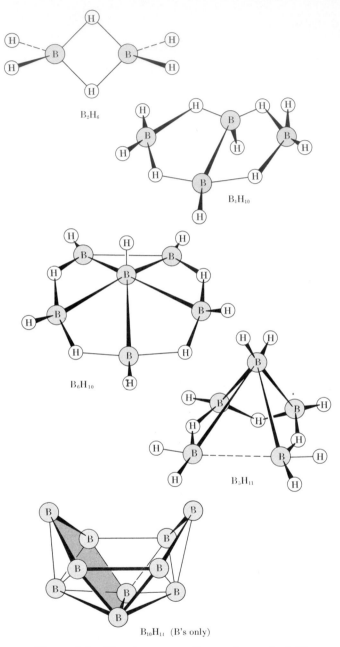

B_2H_6

B_4H_{10}

B_6H_{10}

B_5H_{11}

$B_{10}H_{14}$ (B's only)

Figure 3–1   The structures of some boron hydrides.

52

tile, moisture- and air-sensitive compounds. Their preparative work was completed years before the structures of any of the boron hydrides were known and before an adequate bonding theory was developed. It is interesting to read Stock's book[1] on the chemistry, structure, and bonding of these compounds and to compare this material with the currently available knowledge.

The simplest boron hydride, BH_3, has not been isolated. Evidence has been presented which suggests that it is in equilibrium with the simplest isolated hydride, B_2H_6, but the equilibrium lies far toward the dimeric species. A variety of heavier boron-hydrogen compounds (boranes) have been prepared and the structures of a few are presented in Figure 3–1. Note that the arrangements of boron atoms in B_4H_{10}, B_5H_{11}, B_6H_{10}, and $B_{10}H_{14}$ are fragments of icosahedral units. The particularly unique structural feature of these compounds is the position of certain hydrogen atoms; they are equidistant from two borons but not on a line between them. These are called bridging hydrogen atoms and are found in all boron hydrides.

The bonding in the boron hydrides cannot be described in terms of simple electron dot diagrams. The difficulty in developing a bonding model is that there are insufficient electrons to form two-electron bonds between all neighboring atoms. (Notice that ethane, C_2H_6, for which a suitable electron dot structure can be written (III), has two more electrons than B_2H_6.) To overcome this difficulty it has been necessary to introduce the concept of *three-center bonds*. Three-center bonds contain only two electrons, but this electron pair binds together three atoms. The most

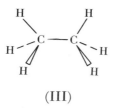

(III)

[1] A. Stock, *Hydrides of Boron and Silicon*, Cornell University Press, Ithaca, 1933.

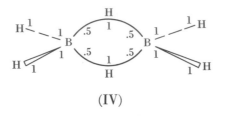

(IV)

common three-center bonds in the boron hydrides link a bridging hydrogen to two neighboring borons. In order to account for electrons in such a system, it is convenient to say that each boron contributes one-half electron and each hydrogen one electron to the bond. Diagram (IV) presents a formal way of distributing the valence electrons in B_2H_6. The shape of the molecule can be rationalized if one visualizes each boron using sp^3 hybridized orbitals. Two orbitals on each atom bind the terminal hydrogens; the other two overlap with the bridging hydrogen's $1s$ orbitals.

Diagram (V) presents a formal electron distribution for the B_5H_{11} molecule. This diagram of the bonding uses two three-center bonds which link three boron atoms. Alternative descriptions can be written including one which uses a five-center four-electron bond to link the five borons. (Note that the molecule is not planar as it appears to be in diagram (V).)

Diborane and tetraborane (B_4H_{10}) are gases at room tem-

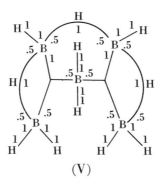

(V)

perature; decaborane-14 $(B_{10}H_{14})$ and other heavy boranes are solids; intermediate boranes are liquids at room temperature. Most of the boranes are colorless. The light hydrides, including B_2H_6, B_4H_{10}, and B_5H_9, have very disagreeable odors.

The preparation of the boron hydrides is a relatively good example of the general methods for the syntheses of hydrogen compounds which were outlined in Section 2–7. The direct combination of the elements, however, does not work in this case. This is presumably due to the lack of reactivity of elemental boron. Hydrogen gas does combine with BCl_3 at about 450°C in the presence of suitable catalysts to produce B_2H_6 and HCl. This is a feasible commercial method but would be difficult to carry out on a laboratory scale. Stock's original method of preparation involved the high-temperature reaction of magnesium with B_2O_3 to give an impure magnesium boride, MgB_2. This material was treated with dilute HCl or H_3PO_4; the reaction produces B_4H_{10} as the major product (in very poor yield) along with smaller amounts of heavier boranes. Diborane is not isolated since it reacts rapidly with water. Stock prepared B_2H_6 by heating dry samples of higher boranes.

Stock's preparative method is now of only historical interest. Reactions of alkali hydrides, $LiAlH_4$, or $NaBH_4$ with a variety of available boron compounds are readily carried out in the laboratory and give good yields of pure products. Two convenient syntheses for B_2H_6 are given in equations 3-2 and 3-3. The heavier

$$3NaBH_4 + 4BF_3 \rightarrow 3NaBF_4 + 2B_2H_6 \qquad (3\text{-}2)$$

$$6LiH + 2BF_3 \rightarrow 6LiF + B_2H_6 \qquad (3\text{-}3)$$

boranes can be prepared by heating diborane under appropriate conditions.

Three types of reaction which boranes undergo are oxidation by air, hydrolysis by water, and formation of adducts with Lewis bases. Like hydrocarbons (natural gas, gasoline, fuel oil) the boranes all burn; the products ultimately formed are water and B_2O_3. The combustion of boranes is considerably more exothermic than that of the hydrocarbons (3-4, 3-5), and therefore considerable investigation has been made on the use of boranes as

$$B_2H_6 + 3O_2 \rightarrow B_2O_3 + 3H_2O + 482 \text{ kcal/mole} \qquad (3\text{-}4)$$

$$C_2H_6 + 3.5O_2 \rightarrow 2CO_2 + 3H_2O + 232 \text{ kcal/mole} \qquad (3\text{-}5)$$

rocket fuels.

The boron hydrides all react with water to generate hydrogen and hydroxy compounds of boron (3-6). This reaction is analogous

$$B_2H_6 + 6H_2O \rightarrow 2B(OH)_3 + 6H_2 \qquad (3\text{-}6)$$

to the reaction of alkali metal hydrides with water. The hydrolysis of B_2H_6 (3-6) occurs very rapidly and hence it must not be exposed to even the moisture in the atmosphere. Many of the heavier boranes hydrolyze very slowly unless they are heated. For example, B_4H_{10} and other hydrides are produced in aqueous solution by the Stock procedure.

The simple and unknown hydride BH_3 would be expected to be a strong Lewis acid, since it would have a vacant low-energy orbital. The fact that BH_3 has not been isolated is almost certainly due to its great tendency to make use of its vacant low-energy orbital; the $2s$ and the three $2p$ orbitals of boron are all used in the bonding of B_2H_6. Diborane reacts with many Lewis bases to give products which are adducts of this unknown monomer (3-7). The heavier boranes form more complex adducts

$$B_2H_6 + 2(CH_3)_3N : \rightarrow 2(CH_3)_3N—BH_3 \qquad (3\text{-}7)$$

with Lewis bases. The reaction of tetraborane with trimethylamine (3-8) gives two adducts. In this reaction it appears that

$$B_4H_{10} + (CH_3)_3N \rightarrow (CH_3)_3N—BH_3 + (CH_3)_3NB_3H_7 \quad (3\text{-}8)$$

a BH_3 group is formed by cleavage of two three-center bonds. The experimentally determined structure of $(CH_3)_3NB_3H_7$ is a distorted variation of (VI). The reason for the distortion is one of the many interesting unsolved theoretical problems in boron chemistry.

The boron hydrides react to give a wide variety of unusual compounds. The reaction of diborane with ammonia ultimately

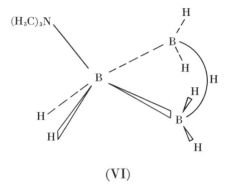

(VI)

yields borazene (VII), a substance which is the inorganic analog of benzene. This substance is similar to benzene in its physical properties but is considerably more reactive. Its reactivity has been attributed to the polarity of the B—N bonds.

An interesting family of compounds is the carboranes, a class of carbon-boron-hydrogen compounds. Some of these were prepared in the search for high-energy boron-containing rocket fuels. One of these, $C_2B_{10}H_{12}$, has an icosahedral framework (VIII).

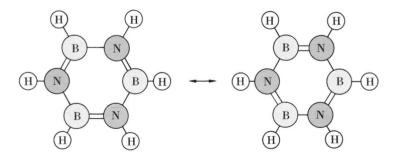

(VII)

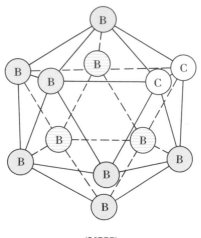

(VIII)

There is one hydrogen bonded to each boron and each carbon. Carborane (VIII) is a chemically stable, reasonably unreactive, white crystalline solid.

SUPPLEMENTARY READING LIST

W. N. Lipscomb, *Boron Hydrides*, Benjamin, New York, 1963. A relatively detailed presentation of the structures and reactions of the boron hydrides.

F. G. A. Stone, "Chemical Reactions of the Boron Hydrides and Related Compounds" *in* H. J. Emeleus and A. G. Sharpe (eds.), *Advances in Inorganic Chemistry and Radiochemistry*, Vol. 2, p. 279, Academic, New York, 1960.

E. L. Muetterties and W. H. Knoth, "Polyhedral Boranes," *Chem. Eng. News*, **44**, No. 19, 88 (1966).

A. G. Massey, "Boron," *Sci. Amer.*, **210**, No. 1, 88 (1964).

D. R. Martin, "The Development of Borane Fuels," *J. Chem. Educ.*, **36**, 208 (1959).

(See Chapter VII for a general reading list.)

PROBLEMS

1. Aluminum oxide will dissolve in dilute nitric acid but boron oxide will not. Suggest a reason for this observation.

2. Suggest possible methods to prepare these compounds: B_2H_6 from $AlCl_3$, BF_3, and any elements; $B(OH)_3$ from B_2O_3 and any elements; borazene from any elements and B_2H_6.

3. Suggest the initial products of the reactions of B_2H_6 with NH_3, OH^-, CO, and PH_3. The compounds formed may undergo additional reactions.

4. A 0.200 liter (at standard temperature and pressure) gaseous sample of B_2H_6 was reacted with with 100.0 ml of liquid water. What is the $[H^+]$ in the solution after the reaction is complete? The acid dissociation constant of boric acid is 6.0×10^{-10}.

5. The anion $B_{12}H_{12}{}^{2-}$ has an icosahedral structure. Molecules or ions isoelectronic (containing the same number of electrons) with $B_{12}H_{12}{}^{2-}$ would also be expected to have this structure. Predict the formulas of other icosahedral molecules. Hint: Replace BH units with isoelectronic atoms or ions.

6. Draw a diagram which distributes the valence electrons of B_4H_{10} in bonds. This diagram will be similar to (IV) and (V).

7. A 1.000-g sample of a volatile boron hydride was burned in air. The products were 2.611 g of B_2O_3 and 1.690 g of H_2O. What is the probable formula of the boron hydride?

8. Calculate the charge-radius ratios of the elements Li, Mg, Ga, Sn, Be, Al, Ge, Sb, B, Si, As, and Te. (Tables of ionic radii are available in handbooks of chemistry and in most advanced inorganic chemistry texts.) Compare the ratios of the elements lying on diagonals on the periodic table.

				C	N	O			
					P				
					As				
		IV			Sb				
					Bi				

Nitrogen

4–1 UNIQUE PROPERTIES OF THE FIRST ELEMENT IN EACH CHEMICAL FAMILY

IN CHAPTER III it was noted that boron is in many ways unlike aluminum, the next heavier element in its family. In general the first element in each family is somewhat unique, whereas the remaining elements in the family are relatively similar with only gradual changes occurring as the elements become progressively heavier. Nitrogen and its compounds are different in many respects from phosphorus and its corresponding compounds; the contrasts are not as pronounced as those between boron and aluminum. Although there are very marked differences between nitrogen and bismuth (the heaviest member of the nitrogen family), the transition in properties from phosphorus to arsenic to antimony to bismuth is gradual and in general regular.

There are several reasons for the unique properties of the first element in each chemical family. Perhaps the most important of these is size. These elements (Li–Ne) are considerably smaller than the elements in the next period (Na–Ar), whereas the differences in size among succeeding heavier elements are not as marked. This feature is illustrated by the halogen-halogen separation in the gaseous halogen molecules (Table 4–1).

Table 4-1
Internuclear Separation in Halogen Molecules

Molecule	Nuclear separation, A	Change in separation
F_2	1.418	
		0.570
Cl_2	1.988	
		0.295
Br_2	2.283	
		0.384
I_2	2.667	

Molecular and crystal structures are markedly influenced by the sizes of the atoms present. Therefore the small size of fluorine normally causes its compounds to have structures different from analogous compounds of the other halogens. Since fluorine is small, more fluorine atoms than those of other halogens can surround a given central atom. For example, silicon and sulfur form the hexafluorides SiF_6^{2-} and SF_6, whereas only the tetrachlorides, $SiCl_4$ and SCl_4, are known.

Since the elements Li–Ne are small, only a limited number of other atoms will fit around them. In fact seldom do these atoms have more than four nearest neighbors (in other words they exhibit a coordination number of four). Heavier elements frequently exhibit a coordination number of six in their compounds. Phosphorus forms the PF_6^- anion, whereas only three fluorines are observed to bond to nitrogen (in NF_3).[1] Phosphorus and arsenic form the phosphate (PO_4^{3-}) and arsenate (AsO_4^{3-}) ions in which four oxygens are attached to the central atom; nitrogen forms the nitrate (NO_3^-) ion. These facts are at least in part due to the small size of nitrogen.

A second reason for the unique properties of elements Li–Ne

---

[1] Very recently it has been reported that the reaction of NF_3, SbF_5, and F_2 produces $NF_4 SbF_6$, a salt of the NF_4^+ ion.

is the presence of only four low-energy orbitals suitable for bond formation. In the elements lithium through neon, the second (*L*) electron shell is being filled. This *L* shell contains the 2*s* and the three 2*p* orbitals and no others. Only these four orbitals, the valence orbitals, have a suitable energy for covalent bond formation. Thus these elements can form only four covalent bonds, and characteristically have no more than four atoms around them in their compounds. The few cases in which there are six are primarily among lithium compounds in which the bonding is predominantly ionic. The maximum four-coordination of the first element in each family can thus be attributed both to the small size of these elements and to the presence of only four orbitals for covalent bond formation.

The heavier elements all have low-energy *d* orbitals which may participate in covalent bonding along with the *s* and *p* orbitals. On this basis one can understand the observation that only four fluorines will form bonds to carbon (CF_4) whereas silicon, the element below carbon in the periodic table, binds six fluorines in SiF_6^{2-}. An important guide in inorganic chemistry has been the octet rule which states that elements frequently have four pairs of valence electrons around themselves in compounds. (In more general terms it may be stated that in most stable compounds each atom has around itself the same number of electrons as a noble gas.) The octet rule is most closely obeyed by the first-row elements; this can be best explained by noting that these elements have four orbitals and only four orbitals in which to place an octet of electrons. The existence of PF_6^- but only NF_3 is consistent with these generalizations (I).

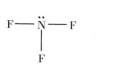

Octet rule obeyed   Octet rule not obeyed

(I)

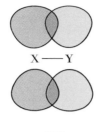

X — Y

(II)

A third and very important characteristic feature of first-row elements is their ability to form π-bonds with themselves or other first-row elements by the overlap of *p* orbitals (II). This type of interaction is responsible for the multiple bonds in many compounds of the first-row elements, three of which are represented in (III). π-Bonds of this type do not make an important contribution to the bonding in compounds of heavier elements. A possible reason for this observation is that only the small first row elements can come close enough together that parallel *p* orbitals (II) can overlap sufficiently to form a strong bond.

The consequences of *p-p-π*-bonding on the structure of compounds of the first-row elements are remarkable. For example, CO_2 has the molecular structure O=C=O, whereas SiO_2 has an infinite polymeric structure in which there are no multiple bonds (no π-bonds); nitrogen, N≡N, and oxygen, O=O, are molecular gases whereas phosphorus and sulfur are polymeric solids, again without π-bonds. The difference in structure between the nitrate (NO_3^-) and phosphate (PO_4^{3-}) ions is certainly

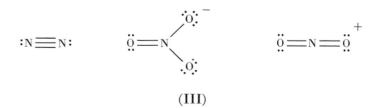

(III)

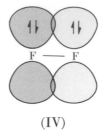

(IV)

due in part to the tendency of nitrogen to use valence orbitals for
π-bonding (III).

A second chemically important characteristic of first-row
elements has been at least partially attributed to p-p-π-overlap.
Single bonds formed between fluorine, oxygen, and nitrogen are
weak and long; since these elements form strong, short single
bonds with most other elements, this has been a puzzling phenomenon. Fluorine, oxygen, and nitrogen atoms all have at least one
filled valence orbital and in fluorine and oxygen at least one p
orbital is filled. Therefore in a molecule such as F_2 p-p-π-overlap
leads to a repulsive interaction (IV); elongation of the F—F bond
will diminish this repulsion between filled p (or hybrid) orbitals.
Similar repulsive interactions may account for the weak and long
bonds in hydrogen peroxide, HO—OH, and hydrazine, H_2N—NH_2.

The weak bonds markedly influence the reactivity of these
compounds. In all three cases, the single bonds are readily broken
to give the radicals $\cdot \ddot{N}H_2$, $\cdot \ddot{O}H$, and $\cdot \ddot{F} :$. The powerful oxidizing properties of F_2 and H_2O_2 result from the easy formation of the
electron-deficient and electronegative $\cdot \ddot{O}$—H and $\cdot \ddot{F} :$ radicals.

<h4 style="text-align:center">4–2   ELEMENTAL NITROGEN</h4>

Nitrogen is the first of the group V elements in the periodic
table. From its position in the periodic table many features of the

chemistry of this element become apparent. As a light element somewhat on the right-hand side of the periodic table it should have and has nonmetallic properties. It exists as a gaseous diatomic molecule (N_2) at room temperature; it is a nonconductor of heat and electricity in the gaseous, liquid, and solid states; it has a large ionization potential (335 kcal/mole) and electronegativity (3.1); and its oxides and hydroxides are acidic.

As a group V element it should exhibit oxidation states from $+5$ to -3 and examples of all are known. As a first-row element it forms a maximum of four bonds, as in NH_4^+. But since nitrogen has five valence electrons, it commonly forms only three bonds and has an unshared pair of electrons, as in ammonia ($:NH_3$). The lone pair of electrons in trivalent nitrogen compounds gives them Lewis base properties.

There are two stable isotopes of nitrogen, ^{14}N and ^{15}N. The more abundant nuclide, ^{14}N (99.635%), is one of very few stable nuclides which have an odd number of both protons and neutrons. A few ratioactive isotopes of nitrogen have also been detected but all decay so rapidly that chemists have made little use of them. In general elements with odd atomic numbers (hence an odd number of protons in their nucleus) have only one or at the most two stable isotopes and only a very few radioactive isotopes with appreciable lifetimes. Elements with even atomic numbers have larger numbers of stable isotopes and long-lived radioactive isotopes.

Since air is 78.09% nitrogen by volume, it is a cheap source of this element. Nitrogen is more volatile (b.p. $= -195.8°C$) than oxygen (b.p. $= -183.0°C$), the other major constituent of air, and thus nitrogen can be distilled from liquid air, yielding a product contaminated with a little argon and minute quantities of other noble gases. Since argon and other noble gases are extremely unreactive, their presence is normally acceptable. Very pure nitrogen can be obtained by careful thermal decomposition of sodium azide (4-1).

$$2NaN_3 \rightarrow 2Na + 3N_2 \qquad (4\text{-}1)$$

The first isolation of nitrogen is attributed to Daniel Rutherford, a physician in Edinburgh, Scotland. He separated nitrogen

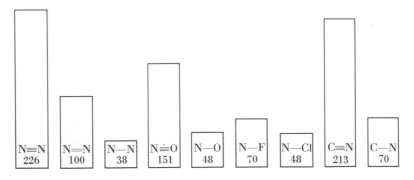

Figure 4-1   The energies (kcal/mole) of some bonds to nitrogen.

from air by sealing a mouse in a bottle of air. After the ill-fated mouse had consumed the oxygen, the CO_2 produced was absorbed by alkali, leaving an atmosphere of impure nitrogen.

In the nitrogen molecule the two nitrogen atoms are linked by a very strong triple bond (bond energy, 225 kcal/mole). This markedly influences the chemistry of the element. Although nitrogen forms strong bonds with many elements, many nitrogen compounds are unstable with respect to decomposition products which include the unusually stable N_2 molecule (Figure 4-1). The very strong $N \equiv N$ bond also causes N_2 to be almost an inert gas. Disruption of the bond requires so much energy that most reactions of nitrogen occur at an appreciable rate only at high temperatures. In marked contrast, certain bacteria are able at room temperature to convert nitrogen molecules into compounds which can be utilized by plant and animal life.

4-3   MOLECULAR NITROGEN COMPOUNDS

The most frequently encountered compounds of nitrogen are the molecular species which nitrogen forms with other nonmetals. The more familiar compounds include those of hydrogen, oxygen, the halogens, and carbon. Many interesting and unusual compounds with boron, phosphorus, and sulfur have also been prepared. Compounds of carbon include amino acids and other substances which are vitally involved in plant and animal systems. Organic and biochemistry texts should be consulted for study of this aspect of nitrogen chemistry.

Hydrogen Compounds of Nitrogen

The binary hydrogen compounds are ammonia, NH_3, hydrazine, N_2H_4, and hydrazoic acid, HN_3. The synthesis and a few properties of ammonia have been discussed in Chapter II. The aqueous chemistry of this molecule has commonly been described as that of the weak base ammonium hydroxide. This impression is readily understandable since neutralization of aqueous ammonia yields ammonium salts and water (4-2). Careful studies, however,

$$NH_3(\text{aqueous}) + H_3O^+ \rightarrow NH_4^+ + H_2O \qquad (4\text{-}2)$$

suggest that aqueous ammonia solutions are best described as containing ammonia molecules. The basicity of aqueous ammonia is a consequence of the ability of ammonia to act as a Brönsted-Lowry base (4-3).

$$NH_3 + H_2O \rightleftarrows NH_4^+ + OH^- \qquad (4\text{-}3)$$

In appropriate solvents such as liquid ammonia, the ammonia molecule can also behave as a Brönsted-Lowry acid (4-4). Very strong bases such as hydride ion are needed to remove an H^+ from

$$NH_3 + \text{base} \rightarrow NH_2^- + H\text{-base} \qquad (4\text{-}4)$$

ammonia. Salts of the amide ion, NH_2^-, are well characterized and are stronger bases than hydroxide salts. Loss of additional H^+'s from ammonia gives the imide, NH^{2-}, and nitride, N^{3-}, ions. These anions are so strongly basic that they are not found in solution, but salts such as Li_2NH and Mg_3N_2 are readily prepared. Amides, imides, and nitrides are counterparts of hydroxides and oxides in oxygen chemistry (4-5).

$$H_2O \xrightarrow{-H^+} OH^- \xrightarrow{-H^+} O^{2-}$$
$$NH_3 \xrightarrow{-H^+} NH_2^- \xrightarrow{-H^+} NH^{2-} \xrightarrow{-H^+} N^{3-} \qquad (4\text{-}5)$$

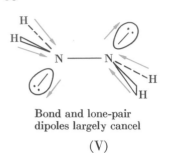

Bond and lone-pair
dipoles largely cancel

(V)

Bond and lone-pair
dipoles primarily add

(VI)

Hydrazine is a liquid at room temperature; it is a weak base and is able to combine with two protons (4-6). It is interesting

$$H_2NNH_2 \underset{H_3O^+}{\rightleftharpoons} H_3NNH_2^+ \underset{H_3O^+}{\rightleftharpoons} H_3NNH_3^{2+}$$
$$K_1 = 8.5 \times 10^{-7} \qquad K_2 = 10^{-15} \tag{4-6}$$

to note that the N—N bond in H_3N—NH_2^+, the hydrazinium ion, is shorter than that in hydrazine itself. This is consistent with the suggestion that the long N—N bond in hydrazine is due to repulsion between lone-pair electrons (Section 4–1). Placing an H^+ on a lone pair reduces the repulsion and shortens the bond.

The hydrazine molecule is quite polar; this suggests that in the most common configuration of this molecule the bond and lone-pair dipoles do not cancel (V, VI). (The arrows represent the dipole moments; the arrow points from the positive end of the dipole to the negative end.) The large observed dipole moment indicates that hydrazine must spend little time in configuration (V); since lone pairs are expected to strongly repel each other, configuration (VI) also seems an unsuitable one. A low-energy configuration may look like (VII); this configuration is consistent with a large dipole moment and yet the repulsion between lone pairs should not be excessive.

The nitrogen in hydrazine has an oxidation state of -2. Therefore one expects that hydrazine should be able to function as an oxidizing agent and in turn be reduced to $NH_3(N(-III))$, and it should act as a reducing agent with the nitrogen being oxidized to a more positive oxidation state. In practice hydrazine is pri-

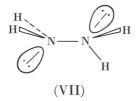

(VII)

marily a reducing agent. The oxidation products observed depend
on the nature of the oxidant and the reaction conditions. The most
common product is N_2.

Derivatives of hydrazine are important rocket fuels.[2] Hydrazine and organic derivatives are particularly suitable for this purpose because their oxidation products are light molecules and their
combustion (4-7) is highly exothermic (a consequence of the stability of the N_2 formed as a product).

$$H_2N\text{—}NH_2 + O_2 \rightarrow N_2 + 2H_2O \qquad (4\text{-}7)$$

Hydrazine is one example of many nitrogen compounds which
have unfavorable heats of formation (4-8). The formation of

$$N_2(g) + 2H_2(g) \rightarrow N_2H_4(l) - 12.0 \text{ kcal/mole} \qquad (4\text{-}8)$$

N—N and N—H bonds in hydrazine is not sufficient to compen-
sate for breaking the very strong $N\equiv N$ bond in N_2 and the H—H
bond in hydrogen. Although hydrazine is unstable[3] with respect
to N_2 and H_2, its decomposition rate is so slow as to be undetectable
at room temperature. An "apparent stability" as a consequence
of very slow decomposition rate is characteristic of many unstable
nitrogen compounds.

Since hydrazine is unstable with respect to N_2 and H_2, it cannot be prepared directly from them. Indirect routes are used, the
most common being the oxidation of ammonia by hypochlorite ion
in aqueous solution (4-9). An intermediate in this reaction is the

---

[2] The most commonly used fuel is unsymmetrical dimethyl hydrazine
$(CH_3)_2N\text{—}NH_2$.

[3] That hydrazine is unstable is a consequence of a positive standard free-
energy change for reaction (4-8).

$$2NH_3 + OCl^- \xrightarrow{H_2O} N_2H_4 + Cl^- + H_2O \qquad (4\text{-}9)$$

very reactive molecule chloramine (4-10), which reacts with more ammonia to yield hydrazine (4-11).

$$NH_3 + OCl^- \xrightarrow{H_2O} ClNH_2 + OH^- \qquad (4\text{-}10)$$

$$NH_3 + ClNH_2 + OH^- \rightarrow H_2NNH_2 + Cl^- + H_2O \quad (4\text{-}11)$$

The other binary nitrogen hydrogen compound is hydrogen azide (hydrazoic acid). It is a weak acid ($K = 1.8 \times 10^{-5}$) and yields the linear azide, N_3^-, ion in solution. Pure hydrazoic acid is a fearfully explosive liquid. Heavy metal azide salts such as $Hg(N_3)_2$ also explode readily and violently and some have been used as detonators for less sensitive explosives. In contrast we have noted that sodium azide decomposes smoothly to N_2 and sodium when heated (4-1). Azides are normally prepared by oxidation of amide salts or hydrazine. A commercial preparation employs N_2O as the oxidant (4-12).

$$2NaNH_2 + N_2O \xrightarrow{NH_3(l)} NaN_3 + NaOH + NH_3 \qquad (4\text{-}12)$$

It is convenient to include hydroxylamine, NH_2OH, in a discussion of nitrogen hydrogen compounds. It is the most common example of a compound containing nitrogen in the -1 oxidation state. The compound has both oxidizing and reducing properties, but is best known as a reducing agent. Like hydrazine and hydrazoic acid, hydroxylamine is unstable. The pure liquid decomposes slowly at room temperature to ammonia, water, nitrogen, and N_2O. Aqueous acidic solutions, however, can be stored at room temperature without much decomposition. The electron dot structure of this molecule (VIII) indicates that it should be a Lewis

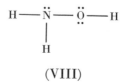

(VIII)

base (4-13). It is a weaker base than ammonia ($K = 1.8 \times 10^{-5}$)

$$NH_2OH + H_2O = NH_3OH^+ + OH^- \qquad K = 6.6 \times 10^{-9} \quad (4\text{-}13)$$

and this can be attributed to the presence of the electronegative OH group which increases the positive charge on the nitrogen and hence makes it less attractive to H^+. Hydroxylamine can be prepared by a variety of methods. One involves a hydrogen reduction of nitric oxide in aqueous acid catalyzed by platinum (4-14).

$$2NO + 3H_2 + 2H^+ \xrightarrow{Pt} 2NH_3OH^+ \qquad (4\text{-}14)$$

Oxygen-Containing Compounds of Nitrogen

Nitrogen forms a series of binary oxides in which all positive oxidation states of nitrogen are exhibited. The oxides are acid anhydrides and oxyacids can be obtained by the reaction of water with N_2O_3, N_2O_4, and N_2O_5. Of the oxyacids however only HNO_3 is appreciably stable. Table 4–2 lists some of the most stable nitrogen oxides and oxyacids. Further investigation of the structure and properties of some of these compounds is still required. Additional unstable nitrogen-oxygen compounds are also being investigated.

Of the nitrogen oxides N_2O, NO, and NO_2 are of industrial importance. Nitrous oxide, N_2O, is known as laughing gas and has been used as an anesthetic. It is slightly soluble in cream and has been widely used as a propellant in "whipped cream" aerosols. It is suitable for both purposes since it is quite unreactive, being inert to substances as reactive as halogens, alkali metals, and ozone at room temperature. The molecule is linear with the geometry shown in (IX). It can be prepared by heating compounds which have the stoichiometry $(N_2O \cdot xH_2O)_n$, for example, NH_4NO_3 or $H_2N_2O_2$.

$$:N\equiv N-\ddot{\underset{\cdot\cdot}{O}}: \quad \longleftrightarrow \quad :\ddot{N}=N=\ddot{\underset{\cdot\cdot}{O}}:$$

(IX)

Table 4-2
Some Nitrogen Oxides and Oxyacids

Oxidation state	Oxide	Name	Remarks	Oxyacid	Name	Remarks
+1	N_2O	Nitrous oxide	Relatively unreactive, colorless gas	HONNOH	Hyponitrous acid	Unstable, weak acid
+2	NO	Nitric oxide	Reactive colorless gas			
+3	N_2O_3	Dinitrogen trioxide	Dissociates to NO and NO_2	HONO	Nitrous acid	Unstable, salts are more stable
+4	N_2O_4	Dinitrogen tetraoxide	Colorless, dissociates to NO_2			
	NO_2	Nitrogen dioxide	Brown reactive gas			
+5	N_2O_5	Dinitrogen pentaoxide	Colorless solid, contains NO_2^+ and NO_3^- ions	$HONO_2$	Nitric acid	Strong acid and oxidizing agent
"+6"	NO_3	Nitrogen trioxide	Unstable, never isolated			

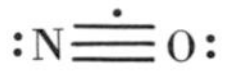

$$:N\!\!\equiv\!\!\overset{\cdot}{O}:$$

(X)

Nitric oxide is a very reactive, colorless, gaseous compound at room temperature. It is one of the few molecules with an odd number of electrons which can be readily isolated. Molecules with an odd number of electrons are not well described in terms of simple Lewis dot structures (X). The nitrogen-oxygen bond order is predicted to be 2.5 by simple molecular orbital theory. This is consistent with the observed short strong NO bond. Dimerization of NO would yield a molecule with an even number of electrons, presumably with structure (XI). This molecule has five bonds which is the same number found in two separate NO molecules.

$$:\overset{\cdot\cdot}{O}\!\!=\!\!\overset{\cdot\cdot}{N}\!-\!\overset{\cdot\cdot}{N}\!\!=\!\!\overset{\cdot\cdot}{O}:$$

(XI)

This may account for the fact that even in the solid and liquid phases there is only a weak association between NO molecules. Most other molecules with an odd number of electrons dimerize readily, but the products normally have more bonds than the separate molecules.

Nitric oxide readily loses one electron to give NO^+. This ion is isoelectronic with (has the same number of electrons as) N_2 and carbon monoxide. Like these molecules a triple bond unites the two atoms (XII). A number of compounds containing this cation

$$:N\!\!\equiv\!\!O:^{+}$$

(XII)

have been isolated, for example, $NO(HSO_4)$ and $NO(AlCl_4)$. None are stable in water, since the nitrosyl (NO^+) cation reacts to give HNO_2 and H^+.

Nitric oxide is prepared on a large scale commercially as an intermediate in nitric acid production. The Ostwald process (4-15) was developed in Germany shortly before World War I and may be

$$NH_3 + O_2 \xrightarrow{\text{catalyst}} NO + H_2O \qquad (4\text{-}15)$$

considered one factor leading to the war. Without a convenient synthetic route to nitric acid, Germany would have found it difficult to produce the explosives necessary for the war. The oxidation of ammonia normally produces N_2 and H_2O, and only in the presence of platinum or other suitable catalysts can NO be made in this way. The direct reaction of N_2 and O_2 is not an effective route since NO is unstable with respect to N_2 and O_2. Since the decomposition of NO is negligibly slow at moderate temperatures, small yields can be obtained by heating a N_2-O_2 mixture to several thousand degrees and rapidly cooling the reaction mixture; some NO can be trapped before it has time to dissociate to the elements.

A characteristic reaction of NO is its rapid combination with O_2 to yield red-brown NO_2 (4-16). In many reactions in which NO

$$\underset{\text{colorless}}{2NO} + O_2 \rightarrow \underset{\text{red-brown}}{2NO_2} \qquad (4\text{-}16)$$

is produced, the observed product is NO_2 as a result of its subsequent oxidation in air. Nitrogen dioxide is an odd molecule with structure (XIII). Molecular orbital theory and bond length and strength data suggest the NO bond order in this molecule is 1.5.

Nitrogen dioxide exists in equilibrium with its dimer, N_2O_4, in the gas phase. Solid N_2O_4 (m.p. $= -9.3°C$) is colorless and

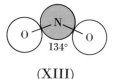

(XIII)

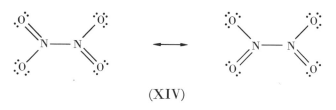

(XIV)

liquid N_2O_4 (b.p. = 21.3 C) is pale yellow, which shows that very little of the highly colored NO_2 is present in these phases. The diamagnetic dimer can be represented by valence bond resonance structures (XIV). This dimer has seven bonds in contrast to six in two molecules of monomer. The structure of N_2O_4 is remarkable in that the N—N distance is 1.75 A, considerably longer than the long single bond in hydrazine (1.47 A). Moreover, N_2O_4 tends to prefer a planar configuration and there does not appear to be free rotation about the N—N bond. Explanations for these phenomena are not apparent.

The reaction of NO_2 with water gives nitric acid (4-17). The

$$3NO_2 + H_2O \rightarrow 2H^+ + 2NO_3^- + NO \qquad (4\text{-}17)$$

NO formed is then air-oxidized to NO_2 and the reaction with water repeated. This is the commercial preparation of nitric acid.

Dinitrogen trioxide and dinitrogen pentaoxide are the acid anhydrides of nitrous and nitric acid (4-18–4-19).

$$N_2O_3 + H_2O \rightarrow 2HNO_2 \qquad (4\text{-}18)$$

$$N_2O_5 + H_2O \xrightarrow{H_2O} 2H^+ + 2NO_3^- \qquad (4\text{-}19)$$

However the reaction of water with N_2O_3 also yields NO, N_2O_4, and NO_3^-. Addition of N_2O_3 to aqueous base does give rather pure nitrite solutions.

Neither N_2O_3 nor N_2O_5 is stable in the gas phase; in fact N_2O_3 is made by condensing an equimolar mixture of NO and NO_2 and the reaction is reversible. Some N_2O_3 is present in the gas phase in equilibrium with NO and NO_2. Dinitrogen pentaoxide decomposes to N_2O_4 and O_2 in the gas phase and is distilled without loss only in a stream of oxygen which contains ozone (O_3).

(XV)   (XVI)

In the solid state N_2O_5 is ionic, consisting of NO_2^+ and NO^-_3 ions. The vapor probably contains O_2NONO_2 molecules. It can be made by removing the water from aqueous HNO_3 with P_2O_5 (4-20).

$$2HNO_3 + P_2O_5 \rightarrow 2(HPO_3)_n + N_2O_5 \qquad (4\text{-}20)$$

Of the several nitrogen oxyacids only two are frequently encountered, nitrous (XV) and nitric (XVI) acids. Nitrous acid is a weak acid ($K_a = 4.5 \times 10^{-4}$). The pure acid dissociates reversibly both in the gas phase (4-21) and in aqueous solution (4-22).

$$2HNO_2(g) \rightleftarrows NO(g) + NO_2(g) + H_2O(g) \qquad (4\text{-}21)$$

$$3HNO_2 \overset{H_2O}{\rightleftarrows} H^+ + NO_3^- + 2NO + H_2O \qquad (4\text{-}22)$$

Therefore the acid is of little importance. Salts of nitrous acid are more stable and aqueous solutions of nitrites decompose only slowly.

As might be suggested by the $+3$ oxidation state of nitrogen in nitrites and nitrous acid, these substances act as both oxidizing (4-23) and reducing (4-24) agents. The oxidation of nitrous acid

$$HNO_2 + H^+ + e^- = NO + H_2O \qquad E° = 1.0 \text{ V} \quad (4\text{-}23)$$

$$NO_3^- + 3H^+ + 2e^- = HNO_2 + H_2O \qquad E° = 0.94 \text{ V} \quad (4\text{-}24)$$

with Ce (IV) or MnO_4^- and its reduction by I^- all occur at a sufficient rate that the reactions are useful for the volumetric determination of NO_2^-.

Nitric acid and its salts are the most important nitrogen-oxygen compounds. Concentrated and dilute aqueous solutions of the acid can be stored without decomposition; they are, however, subject to a light-catalyzed $(h\nu)$ reaction which yields red-brown NO_2

$$2\ HNO_3 \xrightarrow{h\nu} 2NO_2 + H_2O + \tfrac{1}{2}O_2 \qquad (4\text{-}25)$$

(4-25). Nitric acid is both a strong oxidizing agent (4-24) and a strong acid. It is about 93% dissociated into H^+ and NO_3^- in 0.1 M aqueous solution.

Nitrogen is in its maximum $+5$ oxidation state in nitrates, and thus nitrates have no reducing properties.[4] The reactivity of HNO_3 as an oxidant and its reduction products are both sensitive to concentration. Whereas concentrated nitric acid oxidizes many substances rapidly, solutions more dilute than 2 M react negligibly slowly with most reducing agents. A variety of reduction products has been observed. Concentrated nitric acid is normally reduced to NO_2; in dilute solution the reduction is more complete and NO is the most frequent product; dilute nitrate solutions can be reduced all the way to NH_3 by strong reducing agents such as zinc and aluminum. The nature of the product depends on nitrate concentration, acidity of the solution, nature of the reducing agent, and other factors.

A variety of nitrate salts are common chemical reagents. All are water soluble. Nitrate salts decompose when strongly heated. Sodium and potassium nitrates yield primarily nitrite salts and

$$2NaNO_3 \xrightarrow[\text{heating}]{\text{strong}} NaNO_2 + O_2 \qquad (4\text{-}26)$$

oxygen (4-26); most heavy metal nitrates yield NO_2 (4-27). Am-

$$2Pb(NO_3)_2 \xrightarrow{\text{heat}} 2PbO + 4NO_2 + O_2 \qquad (4\text{-}27)$$

monium nitrate decomposes to NH_3 and HNO_3 when gently heated. More vigorous heating produces N_2O and H_2O. At high temperatures NH_4NO_3 detonates, the major nitrogen-containing product being N_2. Although detonation of NH_4NO_3 is most unusual, the explosion of a ship full of this salt in Texas City, Texas, in 1950

---

[4] It is possible to oxidize the oxygen in HNO_3 to give peroxonitric acid, $HOONO_2$.

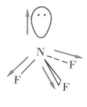

(XVII)

caused enormous damage. Mixtures of NH_4NO_3 with aluminum or TNT (trinitrotoluene) are industrial explosives. Nitrate ion in aqueous solution forms very few complexes with metal ions; therefore nitrate salts are used as "inert" electrolytes in some studies of solutions containing metal ions.

Industrially, nitric acid is used to prepare a wide variety of substances. These include many explosives (such as TNT), nitrate fertilizers, silver nitrate (an important component of photographic emulsions), and nitrocellulose, which is a propellant for bullets as well as a component of lacquer.

Halogen-Containing Compounds of Nitrogen

Fluorine forms a number of binary nitrogen compounds. These include nitrogen trifluoride (NF_3), tetrafluorohydrazine (N_2F_4), two isomers of difluorodiazine (N_2F_2), and azine fluoride (N_3F). Nitrogen trifluoride is a stable inert gas at room temperature. It has a molecular shape like ammonia (XVII) and has a lone pair of electrons. Yet there is no evidence that it will act as a Lewis base. The presence of three very electronegative fluorine atoms apparently increases the positive charge on the nitrogen sufficiently that it repels electron pair-seeking Lewis acids. Nitrogen trifluoride has a very small dipole moment. Since the N—F bonds are certainly quite polar, the absence of a large molecular dipole moment has been attributed to the presence of the lone pair of electrons on nitrogen which provides an electric dipole directed in opposition to the N—F bond moments (XVIII). (The arrows in XVIII represent the bond and lone pair dipole moments.)

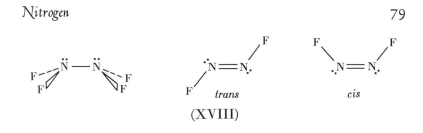

(XVIII)

The other four nitrogen fluorides are all very reactive gases at room temperature. The structure of N_3F is unknown as a consequence of its explosive nature; the structures of the other three are presented in (XVIII). The two N_2F_2 isomers and NF_3 can all be prepared by the electrolysis of molten ammonium hydrogen fluoride, NH_4HF_2; NF_3 is the major product. When NF_3 is passed over hot copper (or other metals), N_2F_4 is produced. This molecule is similar to N_2O_4 in that the N—N bond is weak. As a consequence detectable amounts of NF_2 radicals are present at room temperature. Appreciable concentrations are formed at higher temperatures.

The binary compounds of the other halogens are all unstable; they explode readily, and only NCl_3 has been isolated in a reasonably pure state. The chlorination of an acidic ammonium chloride solution produces NCl_3, an oily liquid (4-28). This compound is a

$$NH_4^+ + 3Cl_2 \xrightarrow{H_2O} NCl_3 + 4H^+ + 3Cl^- \qquad (4\text{-}28)$$

reactive oxidizing agent and is readily hydrolyzed (4-29).

$$NCl_3 + 3H_2O \rightarrow NH_3 + 3HOCl \rightarrow NH_4^+ + OCl^- + 2HOCl \qquad (4\text{-}29)$$

The reactions of bromine and iodine with concentrated aqueous ammonia give compounds with the stoichiometry $NBr_3 \cdot 6NH_3$ and $NI_3 \cdot NH_3$. The former explodes at temperatures above $-70\,°C$. The latter explodes at room temperature. Neither NBr_3 nor NI_3 has been obtained free of NH_3.

A number of halogen-nitrogen compounds which contain oxygen or hydrogen have been prepared. They are in general very reactive substances. These compounds include ammonia deriva-

(XIX)   (XX)

tives in which hydrogens have been replaced by halogens: NH_2F, NHF_2, NH_2Cl, and $NHCl_2$. The bromine and iodine analogs have not been isolated.

The five nitrogen-oxygen-halogen compounds are the nitrosyl halides FNO, ClNO, and BrNO (XIX), and the nitryl halides FNO_2 and $ClNO_2$ (XX). These compounds are all vigorous oxidizing agents and are hydrolyzed rapidly by water. The chlorine and bromine compounds are unstable and decompose at room temperature (note that nitrosyl iodide and nitryl bromide and iodide have not been isolated).

Ring Compounds

Nitrogen forms numerous molecular compounds with other nonmetals. Since there is insufficient space to discuss most of these, we shall mention here only a few compounds in which there are rings of nonmetal atoms. In Chapter III a boron-nitrogen ring compound, borazene, was discussed. Numerous derivatives of this compound also exist, all of which contain six-membered rings with alternating borons and nitrogens.

Phosphorus-nitrogen compounds have stirred much recent research interest. Considerable effort has been put forth to develop polymers containing these two elements. At the moment none of the polymers which have been produced seems to have sufficiently desirable properties to warrant large-scale production. One reaction which yields inorganic polymers is (4-30). Molecular ring

$$nPCl_5 + nNH_4Cl \rightarrow (PNCl_2)_n + 4nHCl \qquad (4\text{-}30)$$

compounds (XXI) and (XXII), and other discrete phosphonitrilic

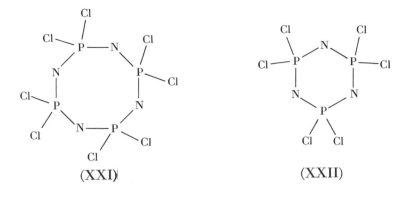

(XXI)   (XXII)

chlorides with the formulas $(PNCl_2)_n (n = 3-8)$ are obtained in addition to polymer. The cyclic trimer (XXII) is planar; in all of these compounds the P—N bonds have some double bond character. Multiple bonding in these molecules requires the use of $3d$ orbitals on phosphorus.

The reaction of phosphorus trichloride with methylamine, H_3CNH_2, gives a compound with several rings. It is likely that it has a structure similar to that of P_4O_6 (XXIII).

Ammonia and sulfur chlorides react to give the unusual molecule S_4N_4 (4-31). The structure of this compound is pictured in

$$6S_2Cl_2 + 16NH_3 \rightarrow S_4N_4 + 8S + 12NH_4Cl \qquad (4\text{-}31)$$

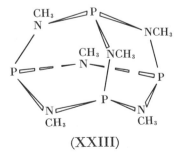

(XXIII)

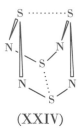

(XXIV)

(XXIV). It is difficult to describe adequately the bonding in this molecule in terms of Lewis electron dot structures. The S—N bonds have some multiple bond character and therefore sulfur d orbitals must be used in the bonding. Moreover, two pairs of sulfur atoms are sufficiently close that there must be weak sulfur-sulfur bonds. The formation of S_4N_4 from the elements is endothermic by 129 kcal/mole; it decomposes explosively to the elements when subjected to a shock. Tetrasulfurtetranitride can be reduced with tin (II) chloride to tetrasulfurtetraimide, $S_4N_4H_4$, which has the structure (XXV).

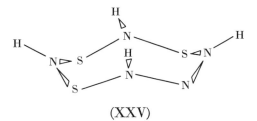

(XXV)

4–4 NITRIDES

The term nitride is applied to all binary nitrogen compounds. In this section we shall consider only nonmolecular nitrides—those with infinitely large structures. These have been divided into

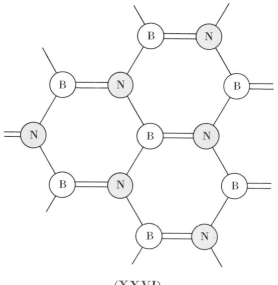

(XXVI)

three classes: covalent, ionic, and interstitial. The prime example of a covalent nitride with an infinite structure is boron nitride. Thermal decomposition of most boron-nitrogen compounds gives this chemically inert, white, slippery solid. Its structure (XXVI) and properties very closely resemble those of graphite (the stable form of carbon) with which it is isoelectronic. When graphite-like boron nitride is subjected to very high pressure at elevated temperatures in the presence of a catalyst, it is converted to a diamond-like structure. This cubic form of boron nitride is very inert chemically and is harder than diamond.

The N^{3-} ion, which one might expect to exist on the basis of the periodic position of nitrogen, is known in a few compounds. It is the only monatomic ion with a charge of $3-$. The alkaline earth metals (Be–Ba) and lithium form ionic nitrides. These compounds are colorless, crystalline, high-melting solids. They react vigorously with water to give hydrolysis products (4-32).

$$Ca_3N_2 + 6H_2O \rightarrow 3Ca(OH)_2 + 2NH_3 \qquad (4\text{-}32)$$

Ionic nitrides can be made directly from the elements or by heating metal amides.

The transition elements form interstitial compounds (see Section 2–6) with nitrogen. These compounds can be readily distinguished from ionic and covalent nitrides, since the interstitial compounds are metallic electrical conductors. The stoichiometry of these compounds, for example, TiN, NbN, W_2N, and Mn_5N, seldom corresponds to that expected on the basis of ionic bonding. Most of these compounds are very hard and high-melting. They are frequently prepared by heating powdered metals to about 1200°C in an ammonia atmosphere. Niobium nitride has attracted considerable interest since it becomes superconducting[5] at 15.6°K. Very few other substances exhibit this property at this "high" temperature.

4–5 PERIODIC PROPERTIES IN THE NITROGEN FAMILY

There is not space in this text to describe the chemistry of phosphorus, arsenic, antimony, and bismuth, the other elements in the nitrogen family. But it is useful to give here some examples of how the chemistry of the heavy members of this family differs from that of the lighter ones. The contrasts in the nitrogen family are particularly vivid.

The physical and chemical properties which we use to distinguish metals from nonmetals change sharply from the nonmetal nitrogen to the metal bismuth. For example, nitrogen is a nonconducting gas; bismuth, a solid with metallic appearance and conductivity. The structures of the elemental solids differ drastically. Solid nitrogen consists of N_2 molecules packed in a crystalline lattice. White phosphorus consists of a crystalline lattice made up of P_4 (XXVII) units. Arsenic, antimony, bismuth, and black phosphorus (the stable form) have structures which consist of infinite sheets of atoms (see Section 1–3).

---

[5] Superconductors appear to have negligible electrical resistance. Currents started in superconducting loops continue to flow undiminished until the superconducting material is allowed to warm up.

(XXVII)

The acid-base behavior of the oxides of these elements is consistent with the change from nonmetallic to metallic behavior. Dinitrogen trioxide and P_2O_3 are the anhydrides of the weak acids HNO_2 and H_3PO_3.[6] Diarsenic trioxide is insoluble in water, but dissolves in aqueous base, a consequence of its acidic nature. Antimony(III) oxide is soluble in both aqueous base and acid (but not in neutral solution) which indicates that it is amphoteric, that it has both acidic and basic properties. Bismuth(III) oxide dissolves only in acids and is a strictly basic oxide.

Associated with the acid-base character is the nature of the species in solution. The nonmetals give only neutral molecules and anions such as NO_2^- and HPO_3^{2-} in solution. Bismuth(III) appears in solution only in the form of cationic species. The hydrated Bi^{3+} cation exists in strongly acidic solution, and hydrolyzed species such as BiO^+ and $Bi_6(OH)_{12}^{6+}$ are important in less acidic media. Arsenic(III) and antimony(III) are less well characterized in aqueous solution, but both cations and anions containing antimony(III) do exist.

The structure of the oxyanions of the elements in their +5 oxidation state also shows a periodic trend. The observed species are NO_3^-, PO_4^{3-}, AsO_4^{3-}, and $Sb(OH)_6^-$. This trend is related to the increase in size of the heavier atoms and their ability to use d orbitals in chemical bonding. The nitrate structure is also a consequence of strong p-p-π-bonding between nitrogen and oxygen. Similar trends are exhibited by neighboring families and in compounds other than oxyanions.

---

[6] Note the change in stoichiometry of the oxyacids of N(III) and P(III).

4-6   THE CHEMISTRY OF THE ATMOSPHERE

To conclude this chapter on nitrogen we shall consider the
chemistry of the atmosphere, an area of applied chemistry which is
of intense and increasing interest. This discussion can be justi-
fied in this chapter since nitrogen-containing species play an important role. The chemistry of the atmosphere is of current interest for two main reasons. Pollution of the lower atmosphere is
a serious problem; this pollution is due to chemicals and chemical
reactions in the atmosphere. The second reason is the space pro-
gram, which has aroused interest in the upper atmosphere, has
created a need for information, and has provided a means to make
detailed studies in space. Studies on the earth's upper atmosphere
will reveal the problems involved in maintaining life in space, will
explain why certain communication techniques are influenced by
changes in the upper atmosphere, and should aid in our fundamental understanding of weather.

The sun is the fundamental source of energy for the earth,
and the radiation that comes from it (and space) is responsible for
atmospheric chemistry. The reactions in the atmosphere result
from the interaction of radiant energy with atmospheric gas molecules. The differences in chemistry which are observed at various
altitudes are due primarily to two factors: the energy of radiation
reaching that altitude and the density of gas particles (the pressure) at that point. The pressure of the atmosphere decreases
rapidly with an increase in altitude. The energy of radiation present also is markedly influenced by altitude. The most energetic
radiation is consumed in chemical reactions in the extreme upper
atmosphere. Lower-energy radiation penetrates further into the
earth's atmosphere before being used in chemical reactions. Only
radiation having energies slightly greater than visible light reaches
the surface of the earth. (Minute amounts of very energetic radiation also reach the earth.) The reactions in the atmosphere provide a vital service for mankind by absorbing lethal cosmic rays,
X-rays, and other high-energy radiation. Table 4–3 indicates the
pressure and temperature of the atmosphere at various altitudes

Table 4–3
Properties of the Earth's Atmosphere at Several Altitudes

Miles above the earth's crust	Pressure in atmospheres	Average temperature, °C	Wavelength of highest-energy abundant radiation, A
0	1	15	3000
10	0.1	−55	3000
30	0.001	0	2000
50	1×10^{-5}	−90	2000
100	1×10^{-9}	800	800
200	1×10^{-10}	1200	800

and the wavelength[7] of the highest-energy abundant radiation at that altitude.

The chemical reactions which account for the bulk of the absorption of radiant energy from space are the dissociation and ionization of N_2, O_2, and O_3 molecules. Each of these reactions requires radiation of a different energy and as a consequence these reactions occur at different altitudes. Since it is very difficult to break the triple bond in N_2, this reaction does not occur at altitudes less than 60 miles and appreciable dissociation occurs only at much greater altitudes.

The double bond in O_2 is more readily broken. Light with wavelengths as long as 1800 A promote this dissociation. Oxygen atoms therefore appear at lower altitudes; at 75 miles equal quantities of O and O_2 are present. Ozone absorbs radiant energy with wavelengths 2100–2900 A; this absorption leads to its dissociation (4-33). This reaction[8] is very important at altitudes around 30

---

[7] The shorter the wavelength of radiation, the greater is its energy. Light with a wavelength of 1000 A carries twice the energy as light with wavelength 2000 A.

[8] $h\nu$ is a symbol for radiant energy.

$$O_3 \xrightarrow{h\nu} O_2 + O \qquad (4\text{-}33)$$

miles. The radiation absorbed in reaction (4-33) is responsible for the fact that the atmosphere at this altitude is considerably warmer than that both immediately above and below.

The atmosphere has been divided into regions on the basis of factors such as temperature and the concentration of electrons (Figure 4–2). The region closest to the earth (0–7 miles) is known

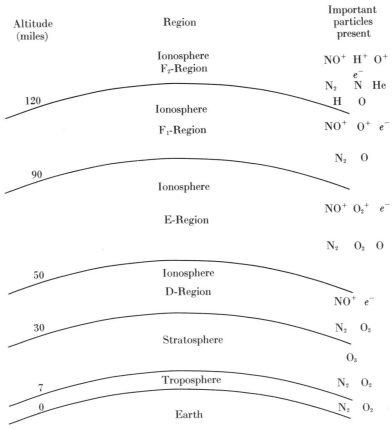

Figure 4–2   Regions of the earth's atmosphere.

as the troposphere. The composition of this region includes nitrogen (78%), oxygen (21%), and small amounts of water, carbon dioxide, argon, and other gases. Current chemical interest in this region is related to the nature of the chemicals which are introduced into the atmosphere by modern society. Substances such as NO_2, NO, SO_2, H_2SO_4, H_2S, and a variety of hydrocarbon derivatives have been identified. Scientists now realize that smog, such as is frequently observed in Los Angeles, is not caused by the initial air pollutants but by the products formed when these compounds react in the presence of radiation from the sun. When hydrocarbons, which normally come from automobile exhausts, are exposed to sunlight in the presence of NO and NO_2, an intricate series of reactions takes place. The products are ozone and a variety of hydrocarbon derivatives. Some of these are irritating and toxic. Although considerable information is now available on the nature and reactions of species in polluted air, this field is complex and much additional research is required.

The next region in space is called the stratosphere (7–30 miles from the earth's surface). The gases found in this region are similar to those found near the earth's surface. The major change is that the fraction of ozone is 250 times greater. (However, it still makes up only a very small part of the gases present.) At these altitudes some radiation is present with sufficient energy to dissociate oxygen molecules (4-34). The oxygen atoms then can

$$O_2 \xrightarrow{h\nu} 2O \tag{4-34}$$

react with abundant oxygen molecules to give ozone; another gas molecule (D) must be present to carry off the energy of the reaction (4-35). As mentioned previously the presence of ozone is im-

$$O_2 + O \xrightarrow{D} O_3 \tag{4-35}$$

portant to our survival since it absorbs ultraviolet radiation and prevents it from reaching the earth.

The region in space beyond the stratosphere is called the ionosphere, since above 30 miles the concentration of ions is appreciable. Only at the low pressures found at these altitudes can species as reactive as ions or oxygen and nitrogen atoms have an appreciable lifetime. At an altitude of 300 miles the concentration of particles is so low that on the average a particle will collide with another only after traveling 12 miles. At atmospheric pressure, a molecule will move on the average only 1×10^{-6} cm between collisions. Since most chemical reactions require a collision between the reactants, rates of reactions in space involving two or more particles will be very slow. Most reactions between reactive particles require a third body to carry off the energy of reaction. Since the probability of the aggregation of three particles in space is very small, this further limits the rate of reactions.

The ionosphere has been divided into four regions on the basis of electron concentration. In the ionosphere electrons are the most abundant charged particle. For example, at 70 miles from the earth's surface there are 100,000 free electrons per cubic centimeter. At the same altitude there are 40 billion oxygen atoms and molecules per cm^3. (At sea level there are 5 billion billion oxygen molecules per cm^3.)

There is still some question about the types and abundances of other ions present in the lowest region of the ionosphere, the D region (30–50 miles above the earth). This is a hard region to study for it is too high for convenient study by balloons or aircraft and it is below the path of earth satellites. There appears to be a variety of ions present. The predominant cation may be the stable NO^+ ion. It is readily produced by irradiation of the trace amounts of NO present (4-36). There are claims that H_3O^+, $H_3O(H_2O)^+$, and other hydrated hydrogen ion species as well as

$$NO \xrightarrow{h\nu} NO^+ + e^- \qquad (4\text{-}36)$$

other cations are present. Negative ions such as O_2^-, NO_2^-, and O_3^- may also exist in the D region. It is thought that these molecular anions cannot survive the high-energy radiation present at greater altitudes, and consequently electrons are the only important anions in the outer parts of the ionosphere.

The next region of the ionosphere (50–90 miles) is called the E region. High-energy radiation frequently penetrates to this region and therefore ionization of the stable O_2 and N_2 molecules is common (O_2^+ and N_2^+ are formed). The abundant cation in the

E region is NO^+. Since very little NO is present in the atmosphere, the primary source of NO^+ in the E region is not reaction (4-36). It can be produced from more abundant species (4-37–4-39).

$$O \xrightarrow{h\nu} O^+ + e^- \tag{4-37}$$

$$O^+ + N_2 \rightarrow NO^+ + N \tag{4-38}$$

$$N_2^+ + O \rightarrow NO^+ + N \tag{4-39}$$

The F_1 (90–120 miles) and F_2 (120 miles and above) regions are the highest regions in the ionosphere. In the lower parts of the F_1 region NO^+ is abundant, as is O^+. In the highest parts of the F_1 region and in the F_2 region helium and hydrogen atoms and ions become important constituents. In this respect these regions resemble the universe (rather than the earth) in composition. In the outer regions of the earth's atmosphere, where the concentration of particles is very small and where high-energy radiation is abundant, virtually no molecular species are present and atoms and monatomic ions are the "stable" species.

SUPPLEMENTARY READING LIST

W. L. Jolly, *The Inorganic Chemistry of Nitrogen*, Benjamin, New York, 1964.

D. M. Yost and H. Russell, Jr., *Systematic Chemistry of the Fifth and Sixth Group Nonmetallic Elements*, Prentice-Hall, Englewood Cliffs, N.J., 1944.

G. J. Moody and J. D. R. Thomas, "Alkali Metal Nitrides," *J. Chem. Ed.*, **43**, 205 (1966).

H. J. Sanders, "Chemistry and the Atmosphere," *Chem. Eng. News, Special Report*, **44**, No. 13, 48 (1966).

(See Chapter 7 for a general reading list.)

PROBLEMS

1. Find the covalent atomic radii of the elements in the boron, carbon, nitrogen, and oxygen families. Compare the sizes of these atoms, and particularly note the small size of the first element in each family.

2. What is the oxidation state of nitrogen in these compounds: N_2O, $NaNO_2$, NH_2OH, N_2H_2, $Al(NO_3)_3$, and NO_2F?

3. Write equations for the reactions used in the industrial production of nitric acid from nitrogen gas.

4. Complete and balance the following equations:

$$Li \ + \ N_2 \qquad\qquad \rightarrow$$
$$\rightarrow NH_4NO_3$$
$$NH_4Cl \ + \ H_2O \qquad \rightarrow$$
$$NH_4Cl \qquad\qquad \xrightarrow{\Delta}$$
$$NH_4NO_3 \qquad\qquad \xrightarrow{\Delta}$$
$$NH_4NO_2 \qquad\qquad \xrightarrow{\Delta}$$
$$\rightarrow N_2H_4$$
$$NaNH_2 \ + \ H_2O \qquad \rightarrow$$
$$Ag \ + \ HNO_3 \text{ (conc)} \rightarrow$$
$$NO_2Cl \ + \ H_2O \qquad \rightarrow$$

5. You are given five unlabeled bottles, each containing one of these gases: N_2, NH_3, NO_2, NO, and NO_2Cl. How would you proceed if you were told to identify each gas and correctly label the bottles?

6. Suggest explanations for these observations: (a) Sulfur forms SF_6, whereas no more than two fluorines will combine with oxygen (to yield OF_2). (b) PCl_6^- and PF_6^- are known, but PBr_6^- has not been observed. (c) The cyanide ion (CN^-) is a common stable ion but CP^- is unknown. (d) The substance produced when magnesium burns in air reacts with water to produce small amounts of ammonia. (e) Elemental arsenic, antimony, and bismuth react with concentrated nitric acid to yield respectively a solution of H_3AsO_4, solid Sb_2O_5, and a solution of Bi^{3+} ions. (f) Nitrate ion is a more powerful oxidizing agent in acidic solution than in basic solution (this is true of oxyanions in general). (g) Free ions are common in space, but are essentially nonexistent at the earth's surface.

7. Calculate the standard electrode potentials for these whole reactions.

$$NO_3^- + 2NO + H_3O^+ \rightarrow 3HNO_2$$
$$2HNO_2 + H_2 \rightarrow NO + 2H_2O$$

8. The ionization energies of N, O, N_2, O_2, and NO are 335, 315, 355, 290, and 220 kcal/mole, respectively. Comment on the type of ions observed at various altitudes in the earth's atmosphere (see Figure 4–2).

								O	F	Ne
								Cl		
								Br		
		V						I		
								At		

Fluorine

5-1 INTRODUCTION

FLUORINE IS THE FIRST ELEMENT in the halogen family. Like other first elements its chemistry differs in several respects from that of chlorine, bromine, iodine, and astatine, the heavier halogens. The differences in the properties of fluorine and chlorine, however, are not nearly as marked as those of boron and aluminum or nitrogen and phosphorus.

Some comparisons between the behavior of fluorine and chlorine were illustrated in Section 4–1. The large difference in the size of the fluoride (1.36 A) and the chloride (1.81 A) ions in particular influences their relative behavior. The small solubilities of certain fluoride salts have been attributed to the small size of the fluoride ion. These sparingly soluble salts include LiF, MgF_2, ScF_3, LaF_3, and the other rare earth trifluorides, and ThF_4 and the other actinide tetrafluorides. The corresponding chloride salts are all much more soluble. The small size of the fluoride ion permits it to come close to a metal ion in a crystalline lattice (see Figure 2–3), and therefore the electrostatic energy binding the crystal together, the lattice energy, is large for fluoride salts.

The small size of the fluoride ion also causes it to interact strongly with water; therefore its hydration energy (5-1) is con-

94

$$F^-(g) + H_2O(l) \rightarrow F^-(\text{hydrated}) + 121 \text{ kcal/mole} \quad (5\text{-}1)$$

siderably larger than that of the other halide ions. This behavior opposes the large lattice energies of fluoride salts and tends to increase their solubility. In fluoride salts in which the metal ion is small or highly charged the large lattice energy dominates the hydration effect and relatively insoluble behavior results.

5–2 PREPARATION OF FLUORINE COMPOUNDS

Fluorine chemistry is a relatively modern field; the element was not prepared until 1886. The difficulty in handling this corrosive element limited subsequent studies; not until the early 1940's were methods developed for the large-scale handling and production of fluorine. Since World War II, fluorine and its compounds have been extensively studied in the search for both fundamental knowledge and for valuable new and useful products.

Compounds of fluorine have been prepared with all other elements with the exception of helium, neon, and argon. Considerable effort has been devoted to synthesis of compounds of these three elements in the last few years, but as yet no success has been reported. Binary fluorides of the remaining elements other than oxygen and nitrogen can be prepared by the direct reaction of the elements. The reaction of fluorine with compounds also ultimately produces binary fluorides (5-2). Fluorine forms very strong bonds with elements and therefore it is energetically favorable to convert other types of bonds into element-fluorine bonds (Figure 5–1).

Reactions of fluorine in general are very rapid and mixtures of

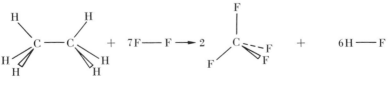

$$(5\text{-}2)$$

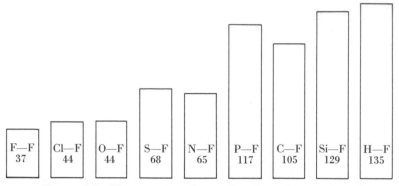

| F—F | Cl—F | O—F | S—F | N—F | P—F | C—F | Si—F | H—F |
| 37 | 44 | 44 | 68 | 65 | 117 | 105 | 129 | 135 |

Figure 5–1   The energies of some bonds to fluorine (kcal/mole).

fluorine with many substances explode.   The reason for the violent reactivity appears to be the ease with which the weak F—F bond can be broken to generate fluorine atoms.   Free atoms in general (with the exception of noble gases) react rapidly.   Direct fluorinations are carried out in some syntheses, but normally the reaction is moderated by dilution of the fluorine with large amounts of an unreactive gas.

Although a direct reaction with fluorine will produce most fluorine compounds, the vigorous character of these reactions and the difficulties in handling fluorine gas have led to the development of other synthetic procedures.   The simplest of these involves the replacement of another halide by fluoride (5-3, 5-4); this is readily

$$(Mg^{2+} + 2Cl^-) + (2Na^+ + 2F^-) \xrightarrow{H_2O} MgF_2 \downarrow$$
$$+ 2Na^+ + 2Cl^- \quad (5\text{-}3)$$

$$3SCl_2 + 4NaF \rightarrow SF_4 \uparrow + S_2Cl_2 + 4NaCl \quad (5\text{-}4)$$

accomplished if a product of the reaction is volatile or insoluble. Hydrogen fluoride is frequently used to prepare fluorine compounds (5-5, 5-6).   When both oxidation and introduction of fluorine is

$$2UH_3 + 8HF \rightarrow 2UF_4 + 7H_2 \quad (5\text{-}5)$$

$$B(OH)_3 + 4HF \rightarrow BF_4^- + H_3O^+ + 2H_2O \qquad (5\text{-}6)$$

desired, it is possible to use any of several reagents which are less reactive and more readily handled than fluorine gas itself. Such compounds include AgF, AgF_2, CoF_3, AsF_3, and SF_4. The last compound is very useful in preparing certain fluorocarbons since it converts

groups. One additional procedure which has proved to be effective is the electrolytic oxidation of substances dissolved in liquid HF. This process is effective in converting C—H bonds to C—F bonds without degradation of C—C or other bonds.

5-3 METAL FLUORIDES

Since fluorine is the most electronegative element, electrons in its bonds with other elements are always more closely associated with fluorine than with the other bonded element. When the other element is not very electronegative, as for example a metal, the transfer of the electron pair to fluorine is essentially complete and ionic bonding is observed. Evidence for the ionic character of metal fluorides includes their high melting and boiling points. These compounds crystallize in typically ionic structures such as that of rock salt (NaCl) and fluorite (CaF_2) (Figure 5-2); they conduct electricity near their melting points and when molten. Aqueous solutions of metal fluorides contain hydrated metal ions and fluoride ions.

Fluoride ion not only forms salts but also complex metal fluorides. It does this most readily with metal ions in relatively high oxidation states such as Fe(III), Al(III), and Nb(V). Complex ions which are known to exist in relatively concentrated aqueous HF include AlF_6^{3-} and BeF_4^{2-}. Complexes containing fewer F^-'s per metal exist in equilibrium with these species. In the solid state very unusual fluoride complexes such as K_2NbF_7

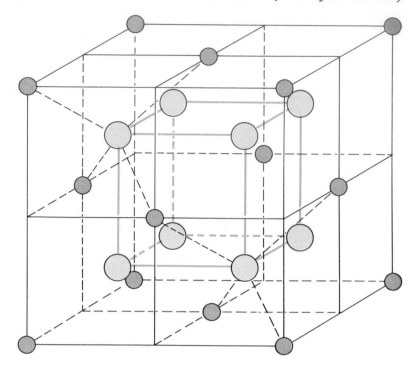

= Ca^{2+}

= F^-

**Figure 5–2   The crystal structure of CaF₂, the fluorite
structure.**

and K_3TaF_8 are known.   The complex ions NbF_7^{2-} (I) and TaF_8^{3-}
(II) are two of the very few discrete species in which an atom is
surrounded by more than six atoms of a different element.   The
small size of fluorine is likely to be responsible for this behavior.

Metal fluorides in which the metal ion has a formal oxidation
state of $+5$ or greater do not have the properties of ionic substances.   This is particularly marked in the metal hexafluorides.

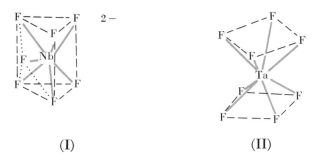

(I)   (II)

Tungsten, for example, reacts with fluorine to give WF_6 (III). This compound is a gas at room temperature. The tungsten fluorine bonds are certainly polar and somewhat ionic, but the fluorine atoms are not sufficiently electronegative to remove six electrons from a tungsten atom. The volatility of this compound cannot, however, be legitimately attributed to the covalent (or ionic) nature of the W—F bonds. It results because six fluorine atoms effectively surround each tungsten atom. The only forces which link one WF_6 molecule to another are van der Waals interactions between fluorines in two neighboring WF_6 molecules.

A number of transition metals form hexafluoride molecules, all of which are volatile. The volatility of these compounds is unusual; for many of the metals, the hexafluoride is by far their most volatile compound. Moreover, the hexafluorides are remarkably volatile when one considers their large molecular weights. Uranium hexafluoride (b.p., 56.6°C; mol. w., 352) is much lower boil-

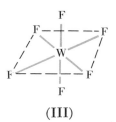

(III)

ing than a hydrocarbon of similar weight ($C_{25}H_{52}$: b.p., 390°C; mol. w., 352). Other heavy compounds with low boiling points are fluorocarbons (C_6F_{12}: b.p., 57°C; mol. w., 338). A characteristic feature of compounds which expose only fluorine to their surroundings therefore seems to be weak interactions between neighboring molecules and a correspondingly high volatility.

Interest in hexafluorides and in fluorine chemistry was stimulated by the Manhattan Project during World War II through the need to separate ^{235}U from natural uranium sources. This separation was accomplished by gaseous diffusion of UF_6. Other actinide hexafluorides (NpF_6 and PuF_6) are known, as are those of the metals Nb, Tc, Ru, Rh, W, Re, Os, Ir, and Pt. Chromium hexafluoride has been reported recently but appears to be unstable at temperatures above $-100°C$. The metal hexafluorides are all very reactive and are good oxidizing agents. Two, PtF_6 and RhF_6, even attack glass at room temperature. These same two compounds are comparable to fluorine as oxidizing agents. The least reactive of the metal hexafluorides readily corrode metals, fluorinate hydrocarbons, and react vigorously with water to produce HF and metal oxides.

5–4   NONMETAL FLUORIDES

A most important fluorine compound is hydrogen fluoride. It is prepared by the reaction of CaF_2, a naturally occurring material, with concentrated H_2SO_4 (Chapter II, equation 2-33). Hydrogen fluoride resembles water in many respects. It is very polar. There are strong hydrogen bonds linking HF molecules to one another in condensed phases; this accounts for its relatively high boiling point of 19°C. Liquid hydrogen fluoride dissolves many salts and a variety of other compounds; it rivals water in this respect. However, the volatility, corrosive nature, acidity, and toxicity of hydrogen fluoride make it somewhat difficult to use. A particularly inconvenient chemical property is its ability to dissolve glass (5-7). Therefore it must be handled in resistant plastic

$$SiO_2 + 6HF \rightarrow SiF_6{}^{2-} + 2H_3O^+ \qquad (5\text{-}7)$$

or certain kinds of metal containers. Reaction (5-7) is useful in that aqueous HF can be used to etch markings or patterns into glass.

An unusual characteristic of hydrogen fluoride is its acid behavior. It disassociates only slightly in aqueous solution and hence is the only weak acid among the hydrogen halides. However, in very concentrated aqueous solution or in liquid HF this substance is a very strong acid. For example, even nitric acid is protonated in liquid hydrogen fluoride (in other words, HNO_3 acts as a Brönsted-Lowry base in this solvent (5-8)). This vast change in acidity is attributed to changes in solvation of the fluoride ion.

$$HNO_3 + HF \xrightarrow{HF(l)} H_2NO_3^+ + F^- \qquad (5\text{-}8)$$

In aqueous solution F^- is solvated by water molecules, but in liquid HF by HF. Very stable species such as HF_2^- and $H_2F_3^-$ are formed (5-9) and this promotes the dissociation of HF. The

$$F^- \xrightarrow{HF(l)} HF_2^- \xrightarrow{HF(l)} H_2F_3^- \xrightarrow{HF(l)}, \text{ etc.} \qquad (5\text{-}9)$$

stability of these polymeric anions is attributed to the presence of very strong hydrogen bonds. The HF_2^- anion as observed in solid KHF_2 is one of the few hydrogen-bonded species in which the hydrogen is equidistant from the bonded atoms (IV). The strength of the hydrogen bond in this anion is about 27 kcal/mole, which is about six times greater than the strength of the hydrogen bonds between water molecules.

The binary nonmetal fluorides are volatile substances, some of which are very reactive (like hydrogen fluoride); others are

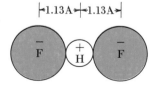

(IV)

amazingly unreactive. In the inert category are the fluorocarbons (CF_4, C_2F_6, C_3F_8, etc.), NF_3, and SF_6. Fluorocarbons are commercially important because of their unreactive behavior. Mixed fluorochlorocarbons are widely used in refrigeration systems. Teflon, a fluorocarbon polymer $(CF_2)_x$, is a very valuable material. It is a stable, nonvolatile, unreactive plastic; an additional useful feature is its smooth surface, which needs no lubrication to give relatively friction-free operation.

That the gases NF_3 and SF_6 are chemically inert is most unusual, since virtually all halides of nonmetals are very reactive, particularly with water (5-10). Sulfur hexafluoride does not react

$$SCl_4 + 2H_2O \rightarrow SO_2 + 4HCl \qquad (5\text{-}10)$$

with steam at an appreciable rate even at 500°C. Since it is energetically favorable for water to react with SF_6 to give H_2SO_4 and HF, the lack of reactivity must be due to the slow rate of the reaction. The fluorines around sulfur in SF_6 must shield the sulfur very effectively from external atoms. Therefore, for this compound to react, one of the strong S—F bonds must break to allow a fluorine atom to escape and an external atom to attach itself to sulfur. Seldom is enough energy concentrated in a SF_6 molecule even at 500°C for this process to occur. A similar explanation must account for the inertness of the fluorocarbons. Selenium and tellurium hexafluorides are successively more reactive than SF_6, although neither reacts rapidly with water at room temperature. The increase in reactivity has been attributed to the fact that six fluorines do not shield these larger atoms from the external environment as well as in the case of the smaller sulfur.

In contrast to these unreactive nonmetal fluorides are such substances as the oxygen and halogen fluorides. There are four oxygen fluorides: FOF, FOOF, FOOOF, and FOOOOF; the latter three are extremely reactive and unstable, and cannot be warmed above -57°C without decomposition. Oxygen difluoride is much less reactive and can be mixed with oxidizable gases such as CO and H_2 at room temperature. Ignition of the mixtures, however, causes violent explosions (5-11). Oxygen difluoride reacts with

$$2H_2 + OF_2 \rightarrow H_2O + 2HF \qquad (5\text{-}11)$$

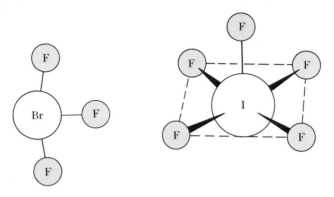

Figure 5–3   The structures of some halogen fluorides.

water at room temperature (5-12).

$$OF_2 + H_2O \rightarrow O_2 + 2HF \tag{5-12}$$

Quite a number of halogen fluorides are known; a few of the most stable are ClF, BrF$_3$, and IF$_5$. These compounds are reactive strong oxidizing agents and behave somewhat like the halogens themselves. They are used as fluorinating agents and react less exothermically than F$_2$. The structures of many of these compounds are unusual (Figure 5–3) and their interpretation in terms of bonding models has aroused considerable interest. Lewis electron dot structures for BrF$_3$ and IF$_5$ are presented in (V). The octet rule is not obeyed for the central halogen in these representations. It is possible, however, to write electron dot struc-

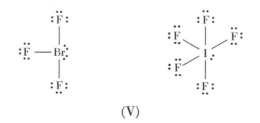

(V)

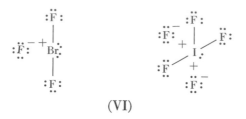

(VI)

tures which obey the octet rule if one considers ionic resonance contributions (VI). The relative importance of the completely covalent (V) and the partially ionic (VI) representations remains an undetermined question. In the covalent structures (V), d orbitals must be employed to hold electron pairs beyond the octet. A related unanswered question is therefore the extent to which d orbitals contribute to the bonding of these compounds.

Bromine trifluoride is a liquid between 9° and 126°C; it has a high dielectric constant and a small electrical conductivity, which suggests that it ionizes slightly. In these properties it resembles water, and it has been studied extensively as a solvent. The self-ionization of BrF_3 (5-13) produces BrF_2^+, the strongest acid in the

$$2H_2O \rightarrow H_3O^+ + OH^-$$
$$\text{acid} \qquad \text{base}$$
$$2BrF_3 \rightarrow BrF_2^+ + BrF_4^- \qquad (5\text{-}13)$$

BrF_3 solvent system, and BrF_4^-, the strongest base in BrF_3. A solution of $KBrF_4$ in BrF_3 can be titrated with BrF_2SbF_6 dissolved in BrF_3 (5-14). This is an acid-base reaction in this solvent. Just

$$KBrF_4 + BrF_2SbF_6 \xrightarrow{BrF_3} KSbF_6 + 2BrF_3$$
$$\text{base} \qquad \text{acid} \qquad \quad \text{salt} \qquad \text{solvent}$$
$$KOH + H_3OClO_4 \xrightarrow{H_2O} KClO_4 + 2H_2O \qquad (5\text{-}14)$$

as KOH and $HClO_4$ each give electrically conducting solutions in water, both $KBrF_4$ and BrF_2SbF_6 make BrF_3 a good conductor. The titration can be followed by noting the decrease in conductivity of the solution as the acid and base react to form the salt.

Salts in nonaqueous solutions normally are weak electrolytes and their solutions are only slightly conducting.

5–5 NOBLE-GAS FLUORIDES

One of the most exciting chemical events of the last several decades was the preparation of the first compounds of xenon. For over fifty years chemistry students had been informed that the "inert" gases were indeed inert. The discovery of compounds of these elements should stimulate student and scientist alike to uncover other invalid hypotheses which lurk in our chemical heritage. The knowledge and techniques which are now available simplify this task, but the chief prerequisite is still the imaginative, alert, and well-trained scientist.

The first noble-gas compound was reported in 1962 by Professor Neil Bartlett of the University of British Columbia. He had previously found that PtF_6 reacts with oxygen gas to give a substance formulated as $O_2{}^+PtF_6{}^-$. He noted from available ionization energies that it is easier to remove an electron from xenon than from oxygen, and therefore felt that PtF_6 should oxidize xenon. The direct reaction of PtF_6 and Xe vapors at room temperature did produce a red substance having a composition which can range from $XePtF_6$ to $Xe(PtF_6)_2$.

Soon after first reports of a compound of xenon appeared, other scientists began synthetic studies. Within a year a variety of xenon compounds had been prepared and characterized in detail. It was found that the direct combination of fluorine and xenon yields at least three fluoride compounds, XeF_2 (VII), XeF_4 (VIII), and XeF_6. There is some evidence that an octafluoride, XeF_8, also

(VII)

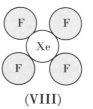

(VIII)

exists, but additional studies need to be performed on this substance. A variety of methods have now been used to make xenon fluorides, but it appears that all employ reagents which will decompose to yield fluorine atoms, which in turn react with xenon gas. The three well-characterized xenon fluorides are all colorless solids at room temperature, but are readily sublimed. It is curious that XeF_6, the only hexafluoride of a gaseous element, is the least volatile hexafluoride.

The xenon fluorides are all reactive. They are excellent fluorinating and oxidizing agents. All of the xenon fluorides react with water. Xenon difluoride yields oxygen and xenon (5-15); XeF_6 yields hydrolysis products (5-16), whereas XeF_4 appears to

$$2XeF_2 + 2H_2O \rightarrow 2Xe + 4HF + O_2 \qquad (5\text{-}15)$$

$$XeF_6 \xrightarrow[-2HF]{+H_2O} XeOF_4 \xrightarrow[-2HF]{+H_2O} XeO_2F_2 \xrightarrow[-2HF]{+H_2O} XeO_3 \qquad (5\text{-}16)$$

disproportionate and to yield xenon and hydrolysis products of $Xe(VI)$ (5-17). These hydrolysis reactions are used to prepare

$$6XeF_4 + 12H_2O \rightarrow 2XeO_3 + 4Xe + 3O_2 + 24HF \qquad (5\text{-}17)$$

oxygen compounds of xenon. The direct reaction between the elements xenon and oxygen has not been successful and it is known that XeO_3 is unstable with respect to decomposition to xenon and oxygen.

When aqueous solutions containing hydrolysis products of XeF_6 are evaporated, the very explosive solid XeO_3 is obtained. Several serious accidents occurred during studies on this compound. From aqueous solutions of $Xe(VI)$ containing KOH it is possible to isolate the stable crystalline xenate salt K_6XeO_6. Oxidation of aqueous NaOH solutions of $Xe(VI)$ with ozone yields perxenate ion, $HXeO_6^{3-}$; Na_4XeO_6 can be crystallized from this solution. Both the $Xe(VI)$ and $Xe(VIII)$ salts are stable when dry. Solutions of $HXeO_6^{3-}$ in strong base are relatively stable, but neutralization causes the rapid evolution of oxygen and the formation of $Xe(VI)$. Even acid solutions of $Xe(VI)$ are relatively stable if reducing agents (including such weak ones as Cl^-) are absent. It seems probable that xenate and perxenate salts will be useful chemical oxidizing agents since the by-product of their reduction, xenon, is gaseous and readily removed from the desired reaction products. Other common strong oxidants, such as MnO_4^-, H_2O_2, and Ce^{4+}, do not always have this desirable property.

Since fluorine reacts directly with xenon, attempts have been made to substitute chlorine. These endeavors have failed and noble-gas chlorides have not yet been reported.

Since the successful preparation of xenon fluorides, considerable effort has been devoted to the preparation of compounds of other noble gases. A few krypton fluorides (KrF_2 and KrF_4) and hydrolysis products have been made. The krypton compounds are less stable than analogous xenon compounds; this may be attributable to the greater ionization potential of the smaller krypton atom. Radon compounds certainly exist and evidence for fluorine compounds has been presented. However, since radon is very radioactive, samples have not been isolated. Helium, neon, and argon have not formed compounds under the conditions which have been thus far utilized. Novel approaches are being applied to the synthesis of such compounds. One unusual approach has been to freeze fluorine and a noble gas in a reaction vessel cooled in liquid hydrogen or helium. Reaction is then induced by ultraviolet radiation. A similar approach to the preparation of helium fluorides involves the radioactive decay of an element embedded in a fluorine-containing matrix at low temperatures. If the decay process produces α particles (He^{2+}), they may react with fluorine to give a helium fluoride, which may have an observable lifetime at the low temperature used.

Many theoretical chemists have become interested in the xenon fluorides. The structure and bonding in XeF_6 has been the focal point of this interest. All other hexafluorides are known to have regular octahedral structures (IX). Although several structural studies have been completed on XeF_6, it is still not certain whether it has a regular octahedral structure or a distorted structure. The relatively high boiling point has been cited as evidence for a structure less symmetrical than octahedral. The two common bonding theories, the molecular orbital and valence bond theories, as they are commonly applied predict different structures for this molecule. The valence bond theory suggests a distorted

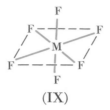

(IX)

structure; the molecular orbital theory, a regular octahedral structure. For other molecules the two theories predict identical (and
correct) structures, and XeF_6 therefore provides a unique oppor-
tunity to test our current theories.

SUPPLEMENTARY READING LIST

A. G. Sharpe, "General Aspects of the Inorganic Chemistry of
Fluorine Compounds," *Quart. Rev. London*, **11**, 49 (1957).
M. Stacey, J. C. Tatlow, and A. G. Sharpe (eds.), *Advances in
Fluorine Chemistry*, Vols. I–II, Butterworth, London, 1960–1961.
C. B. Colburn, "Recent Developments in N–F Chemistry," *J.
Chem. Ed.*, **38**, 181 (1961).
G. H. Cady, "Fluorine-Containing Compounds of Sulfur" *in* H. J.
Emeleus and A. G. Sharpe (eds.), *Advances in Inorganic Chem-
istry and Radiochemistry*, Vol. 2, p. 105, Academic, New York
1960.
R. D. Peacock, "Fluorine Compounds of Transition Metals" *in*
F. A. Cotton (ed.), *Progress in Inorganic Chemistry*, Vol. 2
p. 193, Wiley (Interscience), New York, 1960.
H. H. Hyman, "The Chemistry of the Noble Gases," *J. Chem. Ed.*,
41, 174 (1964).
J. H. Holloway, "Reactions of Noble Gases" *in* F. A. Cotton (ed.),
Progress in Inorganic Chemistry, Vol. 6, p. 241, Wiley (Inter-
science), New York, 1964.
(See Chapter VII for a general reading list.)

PROBLEMS

1. Fluorine has only one stable isotope. Why was this important to the chemists who sought to separate ^{235}U from ^{238}U?

2. Complete and balance these equations.

$$Mg_3N_2 \ + \ F_2 \qquad \rightarrow$$

$$NaF \ + \ Sc(NO_3)_3 \ \xrightarrow{H_2O}$$

$$AlCl_3 \ + \ NaBF_4 \quad \rightarrow \quad AlF_3 \ +$$

$$WF_6 \ + \ H_2O \qquad \rightarrow$$

$$HXeO_6^{3-} \ + \ H_2 \qquad \rightarrow$$

$$KrF_2 \ + \ H_2O \qquad \rightarrow$$

$$KF \ + \ BrF_3 \ \xrightarrow{BrF_3}$$

$$FOOF \qquad \xrightarrow{\Delta}$$

3. Suggest an explanation for the following observations: (a) A weak acid, hydrofluoric acid, dissolves glass whereas hydrochloric acid, a strong acid, does not. (b) The boiling point of HF is 19.4°C; whereas HCl boils at −83.7°C. (c) The product of the reaction of excess fluorine with H_3C—CH_3 is largely CF_4 rather than F_3C—CF_3.

4. The recommended concentration of fluoride ion in water for prevention of tooth decay is 1 g of fluoride ion per 1,000,000 g of water. How great can the concentration of Ca^{2+} be in tap water before CaF_2 will precipitate? The solubility product of CaF_2 is 1.7×10^{-10}.

5. The heats of formation of aqueous HF, H_2O, and H_2SO_4 are 78.7, 70.4, and 216.9 kcal/mole; the heat of formation of SF_6 is 262 kcal/mole. Calculate the heat evolved in the hydrolysis of SF_6. (The heat of formation of a substance is the heat evolved when the substance is prepared from the elements.)

6. The standard potentials for the reactions in which H_2 reduces a series of oxy compounds to the element (other than oxygen) in acidic solution are given below (for example, $2NO_3^- + 2H^+ + 5H_2 \rightarrow N_2 + 6H_2O$ $E^0 = 1.25$ V).

NO_3^-	1.25				
HNO_2	1.45				
H_3PO_4	-0.41	HSO_4^-	0.36	ClO_4^-	1.39
H_3PO_3	-0.50	H_2SO_3	0.45	ClO_3^-	1.47
H_3AsO_4	0.37	$HSeO_4^-$	0.88	—	—
H_3AsO_3	0.25	H_2SeO_3	0.74	BrO_3^-	1.52
$HSb(OH)_6$	0.36	H_6TeO_6	0.69	H_5IO_6	1.3
H_3SbO_3	0.21	$(H_2TeO_3?)$	0.53	IO_3^-	1.2
$Bi_2O_5 \cdot xH_2O$	0.8	$PoO_3 \cdot xH_2O$	0.9	—	—
BiO^+	0.3	$PoO_2 \cdot xH_2O$	0.8	AtO_3^-	1.4

These electrode potentials exhibit a rather complex periodic behavior. Note and comment on at least three trends present in this table of data.

						O	F	Ne
						S	Cl	Ar
		VI				Se	Br	Kr
						Te	I	Xe
						Po	At	Rn

Halogens

6-1   PERIODIC RELATIONSHIPS

SINCE POSITION in the periodic table reveals a great deal about the chemistry of an element, an insight into that chemistry should be based on a knowledge of the element's location in a periodic table. The halogens are on the right side of the periodic table. Only the noble gases are further to the right. The lightest halogen is fluorine; the heaviest, the radioactive astatine; the intermediate halogens are chlorine, bromine, and iodine in order of increasing atomic number.

The halogens are members of group VII in the table, which indicates that they have seven valence electrons. This suggests that they may exhibit positive oxidation states up to $+7$, which implies a possible formal loss of all seven valence electrons. Loss of additional electrons is conceivable, but as yet no compound of any element has been isolated in which electrons beneath the valence shell are lost even in a formal sense. Members of group seven are also expected to exhibit a negative -1 oxidation state corresponding to a formal gain of one electron to achieve an octet of valence electrons. In most compounds assigned oxidation states are merely useful but arbitrary conventions since bonding is predominantly covalent.

The formulas of most compounds can be readily predicted

from the periodic positions of the elements present. This is easily demonstrated with the binary halogen compounds. In compounds with elements having a smaller electronegativity the halogens will exhibit their negative oxidation state, -1. The number of halogens in the compound will therefore be equal to the group number of the other element. For example, with the alkaline earths (group II elements) halogen compounds have the formula MX_2. Elements in groups III–VIII frequently exhibit more than one positive oxidation state, but in general only the oxidation states which leave the element with zero or an even number of valence electrons are commonly observed. (This generalization is relatively ineffective for transition metal compounds.) For example, thallium(I) ([Xe] $4f^{14}5d^{10}6s^2$) and thallium(III) ([Xe] $4f^{14}5d^{10}$) both form chlorides. In group VII iodine(III) ([Kr] $4d^{10}5s^25p^2$), iodine(V) ([Kr] $4d^{10}5s^2$), and iodine(VII) ([Kr] $4d^{10}$) all form fluorides. An iodine(I) ([Kr] $4d^{10}5s^25p^4$) fluoride would also be predicted, and minute amounts of this compound have been detected. The generalization that the only oxidation states which are commonly observed leave the resulting ion with an even number of electrons assures that compounds have an even number of electrons. Very few stable nontransition metal compounds have an odd number of electrons. Compounds with a low-energy orbital containing the odd electron react to fill the orbital; those with the odd electron in a high-energy orbital react to lose it.

Since the halogens are very electronegative, they form only a few compounds in which a more electronegative element is present. Fluorine is the most electronegative element and is therefore always considered to have a -1 oxidation state in its compounds. In compounds with oxygen and fluorine the remaining halogens are formally in positive oxidation states and do bear a fractional positive charge. In these compounds one can normally expect the heavy halogen to exhibit the $+1$, $+3$, $+5$, and $+7$ oxidation states. (These give the halogens an even number of electrons.) This is experimentally observed in the halogen fluorides (ClF, ClF_3, BrF, BrF_3, BrF_5, IF_3, IF_5, IF_7). In the oxyanions of the halogens, the halogen atoms exhibit only the $+1$, $+3$, $+5$, and $+7$ oxidation states; for example, the oxyanions of chlorine are ClO^-, ClO_2^-, ClO_3^-, and ClO_4^-. The halogen oxides, however, do not fit this generalization well; the chlorine oxides are Cl_2O, ClO_2, Cl_2O_6, and Cl_2O_7. In general the halogen oxides are unstable (particularly those which do not fit the rule) and are relatively unimportant. They do illustrate the fact that there are exceptions to virtually all generalizations.

6-2 PROPERTIES OF THE HALOGENS

The halogens exist in nature primarily as halide salts; these are found in all bodies of water, but are relatively concentrated in the oceans and in lakes such as the Great Salt Lake and the Dead Sea. Deposits of salt are also found where ancient seas evaporated to dryness. Iodine is found in deposits of iodate (IO_3^-) salts. The free elements are good oxidizing agents and hence do not survive as such in nature.

Fluorine and chlorine are yellow-green gases, bromine is a red-brown liquid, and iodine is a violet-black solid at room temperature. The halogens all exist as diatomic, X_2, molecules in both the gaseous and condensed states. The liquids and solutions of the elements in solvents with which they do not react are nonconducting. These properties indicate that the halogens are prime examples of nonmetals.

Since the halogens are excellent oxidizing agents, their preparation from the naturally occurring halides requires the use of strong oxidants. Fluorine is the strongest known oxidizing agent and hence can only be produced by electrolysis. Commercially it is prepared by electrolysis of liquid HF to which KF is added as the electrolyte (6-1). (Pure HF, like pure water, is a poor con-

$$2HF(l) \xrightarrow[KF]{elec.} H_2 + F_2 \qquad (6-1)$$

ductor of electricity.) Water or other oxidizable material must be absent or it will be oxidized in preference to fluoride. Chlorine is produced commercially by electrolysis; chloride ion is oxidized at sufficiently low potentials that aqueous solutions can be used without the evolution of much oxygen (6-2). Chlorine is also pro-

$$2Cl^-(aqueous) + H_2O \xrightarrow{\text{elec.}} Cl_2(g) + H_2 + 2OH^- \quad (6\text{-}2)$$

duced by the electrolysis of molten sodium chloride (6-3).   This reaction is the commercial source of sodium metal.   Chlorine is also

$$2NaCl(l) \xrightarrow{\text{elec.}} 2Na + Cl_2(g) \quad\quad (6\text{-}3)$$

obtained as a by-product of the electrolytic preparation of calcium and magnesium.

Bromine is normally prepared by chlorine oxidation of bromide solutions (6-4); sea water contains enough bromide ion to make it

$$Br^-(aqueous) + Cl_2(g) \to Br_2 + Cl^-(aqueous) \quad (6\text{-}4)$$

the commercial source of bromine.   The very cheap oxidizing agent sulfuric acid, H_2SO_4, will convert iodide to iodine (6-5).

$$8H^+ + 8I^- + H_2SO_4 \to 4I_2 + H_2S + 4H_2O \quad (6\text{-}5)$$

Iodate salts can be reduced to iodine by the inexpensive reducing agent SO_2 (6-6).

$$2IO_3^- + 5SO_2 + 4H_2O \to I_2 + 5SO_4^{2-} + 8H^+ \quad (6\text{-}6)$$

In the laboratory, chlorine, bromine, and iodine can be easily prepared by the reaction of acidic halide solutions with MnO_2 (6-7).   Manganese dioxide is too expensive for the commercial

$$MnO_2 + 2X^- + 4H^+ \to Mn^{2+} + X_2 + 2H_2O \quad (6\text{-}7)$$

preparation of halogens, but is an easily handled strong oxidizing agent.

6–3   REACTIONS OF THE HALOGENS

All of the halogens are reactive and combine directly with most elements.   The direct reaction of the two elements is frequently the convenient way to prepare a pure binary halide. Fluorine reacts most vigorously and with the greatest number of elements and compounds.   Fluorine also tends to produce binary compounds which contain the largest ratio of halogen to the other atom; in these compounds the atom combined with fluorine frequently exhibits a higher oxidation state than in its compounds with the other halogens. An example of this behavior is the reactions of vanadium with the halogens; the products are VF_5, VCl_4, VBr_3, and VI_3.

The halogens also react with many compounds. Since water is the compound most frequently used by chemists (and other people as well), its reactions with the halogens are of particular interest. These reactions also illustrate very well the utility and limitations of tables of half-cell redox potentials in predicting chemical behavior. Table 6-1 presents the necessary redox poten-

Table 6-1
Electrode Potentials[a] for Some Half-Cell Reactions Important in Halogen Chemistry

Acid Solution

$$O_2 \xrightarrow{1.23} H_2O$$
$$F_2 \xrightarrow{3.06} HF$$
$$ClO_4^- \xrightarrow{1.19} ClO_3^- \xrightarrow{1.21} HClO_2 \xrightarrow{1.65} HOCl \xrightarrow{1.63} Cl_2 \xrightarrow{1.36} Cl^-$$
$$BrO_3^- \xrightarrow{1.50} \qquad HOBr \xrightarrow{1.60} Br_2 \xrightarrow{1.07} Br^-$$
$$H_5IO_6 \xrightarrow{1.60} IO_3 \xrightarrow{1.14} \qquad HOI \xrightarrow{1.45} I_2 \xrightarrow{0.54} I^-$$
$$AtO_3^- \xrightarrow{1.4} \qquad HOAt \xrightarrow{0.7} At_2 \xrightarrow{-0.2} At^-$$

Basic Solution

$$O_2 \xrightarrow{0.40} H_2O$$
$$F_2 \xrightarrow{2.87} F^-$$
$$ClO_4^- \xrightarrow{0.36} ClO_3^- \xrightarrow{0.33} ClO_2^- \xrightarrow{0.66} ClO^- \xrightarrow{0.89} Cl_2 \xrightarrow{1.36} Cl^-$$
$$BrO_3^- \xrightarrow{0.46} \qquad BrO^- \xrightarrow{0.76} Br_2 \xrightarrow{1.07} Br^-$$
$$H_3IO_6^{2-} \xrightarrow{0.7} IO_3^- \xrightarrow{0.13} \qquad IO^- \xrightarrow{0.49} I_2 \xrightarrow{0.54} I^-$$
$$AtO_3^- \xrightarrow{0.5} \qquad AtO^- \xrightarrow{0.0} At_2 \xrightarrow{-0.2} At^-$$

[a] $ClO_4^- \xrightarrow{1.19} ClO_3^-$ in acid solution means that the standard half-cell potential for the balanced half-reaction which converts ClO_4^- into ClO_3^- in acid solution (6-8) is 1.19 V. $ClO_4^- \xrightarrow{0.36} ClO_3^-$ in basic solution means that the standard potential for half-cell reaction (6-9) is 0.36 V.

$$ClO_4^- + 2H^+ + 2e^- = ClO_3^- + H_2O \qquad (6\text{-}8)$$
$$ClO_4^- + H_2O + 2e^- = ClO_3^- + 2OH^- \qquad (6\text{-}9)$$

tial data. In using standard electrode potentials one should remember that the values cited apply exactly only when the activity[1] of each species is 1.00.

From the potential table it is possible to determine which of the halogens can oxidize water. In acid solution only half-cells with potentials greater than 1.23 V can convert water to oxygen, and therefore both fluorine and chlorine are able to oxidize water (6-10). In practice only half-cells with potentials greater than

$$2(F_2 + 2H^+ + 2e^- = 2HF) \qquad E^0 = 3.06 \text{ V}$$
$$-(O_2 + 4H^+ + 4e^- = 2H_2O) \qquad E^0 = 1.23 \text{ V}$$
$$\overline{2F_2 + 2H_2O = 4HF + O_2} \qquad E^0 = 1.83 \text{ V} \qquad (6\text{-}10)$$

1.8 V oxidize water at an appreciable rate. Fluorine does react rapidly. Chlorine will produce oxygen from water but the reaction is slow and can normally be neglected. Bromine and iodine cannot oxidize water in acidic solution.

In strongly basic solution a half-cell with a potential greater than 0.40V is able to oxidize water to oxygen, but only half-cells with potentials greater than 0.9 V do so at a rapid rate. All halogens other than astatine are thus able to generate oxygen from water. Fluorine does react with basic aqueous solution but the predominant product is OF_2; the other halogens also react in basic aqueous solution but again oxygen is not an important product. These reactions illustrate a few of the many instances in nonmetal chemistry in which kinetic factors determine the products of reactions. Energy factors[2] favor the oxidation of water, but this reaction is slow.

In Table 6–1 one can see that bromine in basic solution is a

---

[1] The activity of a species in solution is approximately equal to its molarity. To achieve an activity of one, the molar concentration normally has to be moderately greater than one. The activity of a gas is very nearly equal to its partial pressure expressed in atmospheres.

[2] The standard potential for a reaction is directly proportional to the standard free energy (ΔG^0) for that reaction. The magnitude of the free energy change alone determines whether a reaction can occur. If the cell potential for a reaction is positive, the free energy change for the reaction is favorable and the reaction will occur; the reaction may be infinitely slow however. If the cell potential is negative, the reaction will proceed in the opposite direction; again the rate may be slow.

better oxidant than BrO^-. Therefore one expects bromine to oxidize and reduce itself (disproportionate) to BrO^- and Br^- (6-11). From the standard potential for the reaction (0.31 V) one can calculate the equilibrium constant for the reaction at 25°C by means

$$\begin{array}{llr} \tfrac{1}{2}Br_2 + e^- = & Br^- & E^0 = 1.07\ \text{V} \\ -(BrO^- + H_2O + e^- = \tfrac{1}{2}Br_2 + 2OH^-) & & E^0 = 0.76\ \text{V} \\ \hline Br_2\ + 2OH^- \quad = BrO^- + H_2O & & E^0 = 0.31\ \text{V} \end{array} \quad (6\text{-}11)$$

of equation (6-12).[3] The equilibrium constant shows that bromine

$$\log K = 17nE^0$$
$$\log K = \log \frac{[BrO^-]\ [Br^-]}{[Br_2]\ [OH^-]} = 17(1)(0.31) = 5.3$$
$$K = \frac{[BrO^-]\ [Br^-]}{[Br_2]\ [OH^-]} = 2 \times 10^5 \qquad (6\text{-}12)$$

in basic solution is largely converted into bromide and hypobromite ions. Moreover, the extent of this conversion increases as the square of the hydroxide concentration. This disproportionation reaction is rapid; therefore it is observed rather than oxidation of water by bromine. The ions, BrO^- and BrO_3^-, are both able to generate oxygen from water (see the potentials in Table 6-1), but once again the rates of these oxidations are slow and the reactions are not important.

The reaction does not stop at this stage. Hypobromite ion is a better oxidizing agent than bromate, and therefore an additional disproportionation can occur (6-13). The bromine formed will in turn disproportionate and thus BrO_3^- and Br^- are the ulti-

$$\begin{array}{llr} 2(2BrO^- + 2H_2O + 2e^- = Br_2\ + 4OH^-) & & E^0 = 0.76\ \text{V} \\ -(BrO_3^- + 2H_2O + 4e^- = BrO^- + 4OH^-) & & E^0 = 0.46\ \text{V} \\ \hline 5BrO^-\ + 2H_2O \quad = BrO_3^- + 2Br_2 + 4OH^- & & E^0 = 0.30\ \text{V} \end{array}$$
$$(6\text{-}13)$$

mate products. The disproportionation of BrO^- is rapid at 25°C; therefore solutions of OBr^- can be obtained by the reaction of Br_2

---

[3] Equation (6-12) was derived from this equation: $\log K = nFE^0/2.303\ RT$. F is the faraday (96,500 coulombs/mole), R is the gas constant, T is the absolute temperature, and n is the number of electrons involved in the redox process.

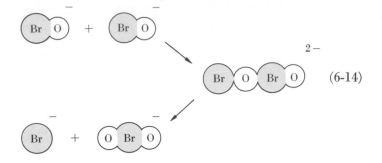

(6-14)

with basic aqueous solutions only at 0°C. At this temperature OBr⁻ disproportionates slowly.

Equation (6-13) implies that the disproportionation of BrO⁻ yields bromine and bromate ion. The observed products are bromide and bromate ions; their formation can be explained in terms of subsequent disproportionation of the bromine. Since the potentials for both reactions (6-11) and (6-13) are positive, this is a plausible explanation for the observed products. However, it need not be correct. It is probable that bromine is not an intermediate in the disproportionation of BrO⁻. There is considerable evidence that many oxidations by oxyanions occur by oxygen atom transfer (6-14). Thus the initial products of disproportionation are likely to be bromide and bromite ions. Bromite ion has not been observed in solution and presumably reacts rapidly to give bromate ion (6-15).

From this analysis of the reactions of bromine in basic aqueous

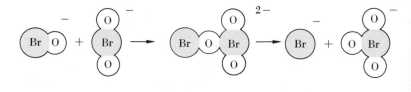

(6-15)

solution we should recognize several things about the use of redox potential data. From potential data we can predict whether a reaction can occur; we predicted that bromine and hypobromite ion would disproportionate and they do. In addition, from the potential data, the equilibrium constants for reactions can be calculated. However, care must be taken in using potential tables. We found that by combining half-cells, we could predict that reactions can occur which in practice are not important. Reactions that can occur do not because other reactions proceed at greater rates. This is the reason that bromine and hypobromite disproportionate in solution rather than liberating oxygen; this would be the reason why BrO^- may disproportionate to BrO_3^- and Br^- without the formation of bromine as an intermediate.

In acidic solution bromine is too weak an oxidant to produce oxygen from water. However, both hypobromous acid and bromate ion can oxidize water. Solutions of hypobromous acid are unstable, but react primarily to give bromate and bromide ions. Bromate ion oxidizes water at a negligibly slow rate in the absence of catalysts. In general it has been observed that in a series of oxyanions like XO^{n-}, XO_2^{n-}, XO_3^{n-}, and XO_4^{n-}, the ions with the largest number of oxygens react most slowly. This phenomenon, like the lack of reactivity of CF_4 and SF_6, may result because of the screening effect of the external atoms.

Bromine is a weaker oxidizing agent than HOBr and hence it cannot disproportionate into HOBr and Br^- in acid solution (6-16). As a consequence bromine dissolves in acidified water with no further reaction.

$$
\begin{array}{lll}
Br_2 + 2e^- = 2Br^- & E^0 = & 1.07 \text{ V} \\
-(2BrO^- + 4H^+ + 2e^- = Br_2 + 2H_2O) & E^0 = & 1.60 \text{ V} \\
\hline
2Br_2 + 2H_2O = 2BrO^- + 2Br^- + 4H^+ & E^0 = & -0.53 \text{ V}
\end{array}
$$

$$(6\text{-}16)$$

The reactions of the other halogens with water will not be described here; however, sufficient data are presented in the problems after this chapter to allow the reader to predict the products arising from all the halogens in acidic or basic aqueous solution.

Although most of the reactions of the halogens must be

omitted for lack of space, the reaction of iodine with thiosulfate
ion is worthy of mention (6-17). This reaction is widely used in

$$I_2 + 2S_2O_3{}^{2-} \rightarrow 2I^- + S_4O_6{}^{2-} \qquad (6\text{-}17)$$

the quantitative analysis of a variety of oxidizing and reducing
agents. Reaction (6-17) is performed in aqueous solution. Since
iodine is relatively insoluble in water, aqueous iodide solutions are
used in which iodine readily dissolves with the formation of triiodide ion (6-18). Standardized thiosulfate solutions are used to

$$I_2 + I^- \rightleftharpoons I_3{}^- \qquad (6\text{-}18)$$

titrate the triiodide ion normally generated by the reaction of
excess iodide ion with the oxidant to be analyzed. Iodate ion can
be analyzed in this way since both reactions (6-17) and (6-19) are
rapid and complete.

$$IO_3{}^- + 8I^- + 6H^+ \rightarrow 3I_3{}^- + 3H_2O \qquad (6\text{-}19)$$

The mechanism of the reaction of triiodide ion with $S_2O_3{}^{2-}$
has been studied and provides an example of the way in which a
halogen can oxidize a suitable reducing agent. The first step in
the postulated mechanism is an equilibrium in which I^+ is trans-
ferred to a $S_2O_3{}^{2-}$ ion (6-20). The observed products of reaction

$$
\text{III}^- + \underset{\underset{O}{|}}{\overset{\overset{O}{|}}{\text{SSO}}}{}^{2-} \underset{\text{fast}}{\rightleftharpoons} \text{III}\!-\!\underset{\underset{O}{|}}{\overset{\overset{O}{|}}{\text{SSO}}}{}^{3-} \underset{\text{fast}}{\rightleftharpoons} 2I^- + \underset{\underset{O}{|}}{\overset{\overset{O}{|}}{\text{ISSO}}}{}^- \qquad (6\text{-}20)
$$

(6-19) are thought to arise from a slow reaction between $S_2O_3{}^{2-}$
and $IS_2O_3{}^-$ (6-21). Oxidations by halogens may in many cases be

$$
\underset{\underset{O}{|}}{\overset{\overset{O}{|}}{\text{OSS}}}{}^{2-} + \underset{\underset{O}{|}}{\overset{\overset{O}{|}}{\text{ISSO}}}{}^- \xrightarrow{\text{slow}} \underset{\underset{O}{|}}{\overset{\overset{O}{|}}{\text{OSS}}}\!\!-\!\!\overset{I}{\underset{\underset{O}{|}}{\overset{\overset{O}{\diagdown|}}{\text{SSO}}}}{}^{3-} \rightarrow \underset{\underset{O\,O}{|\,|}}{\overset{\overset{O\,O}{|\,|}}{\text{OSSSSO}}}{}^{2-} + I^- \qquad (6\text{-}21)
$$

visualized as arising from the dissociation of X_2 into X^+ and X^-
with the transfer of X^+. In Chapter II two other routes for the

reduction of halogens were illustrated in the discussion of the reactions of hydrogen with the halogens.

6–4 HALOGEN COMPOUNDS WITH NONMETALS

Many nonmetal halides exist; some have been mentioned in
earlier chapters and some in earlier sections of this chapter. A
few additional important compounds and ones exhibiting interesting properties will be discussed here.

In Section 6–3 the reactions of halogens with aqueous base
were discussed. The products of these reactions include many of
the oxyanions of the halogens. (The naming of oxyacids and oxyanions is illustrated in Table 6-2.) The properties of a few of these
compounds merit further discussion. Hypochlorite ion (OCl^-)
is an important and common bleaching agent. It was noted earlier
that in the disproportionation of OBr^- in basic solution the mechanism probably involves transfer of an oxygen atom. Direct evidence for oxygen atom transfer has been found in the oxidation of
nitrite ion by hypochlorite ion. When the hypochlorite ion initially
contains labeled oxygen (either ^{17}O or ^{18}O), it has been found that

Table 6–2
Names of Oxyhalogen Acids and Anions

Oxidation state of halogen	Formula of acid	Name of acid	Name of anion	Example
+1	HXO	*Hypo*halous acid	*Hypo*hal*ite* ion	Hypobromous acid($HBrO$)
+3	HXO_2	Hal*ous* acid	Hal*ite* ion	Chlorite ion (ClO_2^-)
+5	HXO_3	Hal*ic* acid	Hal*ate* ion	Iodate ion (IO_3^-)
+7	$HXO_4{}^a$	*Per*hal*ic* acid	*Per*hal*ate* ion	Perchloric acid($HClO_4$)

[a] Periodic acid has the formula H_5IO_6. This species which contains two
more water molecules than HXO_4 is known as ortho-periodic acid.

the labeled oxygen ultimately is found in the oxidized product, nitrate ion (6-22). Similar instances of labeled oxygen transfer have been observed in oxidations with other oxyanions.

$$*OCl^- + NO_2^- \rightarrow Cl^- + *ONO_2^- \qquad (6\text{-}22)$$

Perchlorate ion (ClO_4^-) is the anion of the strongest common acid, $HClO_4$. Perchlorate ion not only binds H^+ very weakly but virtually never forms complexes with metal ions in aqueous solution. For this reason perchlorate salts are frequently used in solution studies when the anion of other salts might form objectionable complexes with metal ions present. Perchlorate ion is potentially a very powerful oxidizing agent. Concentrated perchloric acid and other perchlorates have been known to cause violent explosions when exposed to organic matter or other reducing agents. Perchlorate ion is used as an oxidant in certain solid rocket fuels; an important one currently in use is a mixture of ammonium perchlorate and aluminum (this is potentially a very hazardous mixture). Surprisingly, dilute perchlorate solutions do not cause the oxidation of many good reducing agents. In fact metals such as zinc and aluminum dissolve in dilute perchlorate solutions with the evolution of hydrogen. The perchlorate ion in dilute solutions at room temperature reacts very slowly with these metals even though the reactions are potentially very exothermic.

Table 6-1 presents several facts about the oxyanions which are worthy of comment. Periodate ion (I) is structurally different

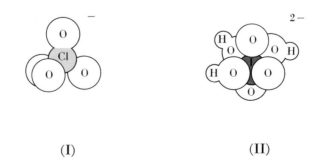

(I)   (II)

from perchlorate ion (II); there are six oxygens about the iodine but only four around chlorine. The increase in coordination number is normally attributed to the greater size of iodine; more oxygens, therefore, fit around it. This is a periodic phenomenon since the oxyacids of antimony and tellurium in their highest oxidation states (H_7SbO_6 and H_6TeO_6) both contain six oxygens, whereas those of arsenic and selenium (H_3AsO_4 and H_2SeO_4) contain only four. It should be noted that the IO_4^- ion is in equilibrium with H_5IO_6 in aqueous solution (6-23), but the equilibrium favors the six coordinated species in acid solution.

$$H_5IO_6 \rightleftarrows H^+ + IO_4^- + 2H_2O \qquad K = 0.04 \qquad (6\text{-}23)$$

Table 6-1 gives no data for perbromate ion, for this species has not been prepared. The nonexistence of BrO_4^- or $H_3BrO_6^{2-}$ may be related to the change in geometry observed in passing from perchlorate to periodate. Evidently neither four- nor six-coordination gives a suitably stable structure to perbromate.

In Chapter IV we became acquainted with the halogen fluorides. These compounds are members of a larger group of compounds called *interhalogens*. The nonfluorine-containing interhalogens are ICl_3, ICl, IBr, and $BrCl$. The diatomic molecules behave much like halogens and have properties intermediate between those of the halogens from which they are prepared. The heaviest halogen (the least electronegative one) bears a partial positive charge in these compounds and is located in the center of those compounds which contain more than two atoms (see Figure 5-3).

Related to the interhalogens are a series of polyhalide ions. The only frequently encountered polyhalide is the triiodide ion which forms readily when iodine is added to aqueous iodide solutions (6-18). Polyiodides with the stoichiometries I_3^-, I_5^-, I_7^-, and I_9^- are known but all except I_3^- are relatively unstable. Mixed polyhalides such as ICl_4^- are also known. The polyhalide ions contain an odd number of halogen atoms. A singly negative polyhalide ion with an even number of atoms would be an *odd molecule* (one which contains an odd number of electrons).

The triiodide ion is one of a number of adducts of iodine with Lewis bases. In an iodine molecule each atom has an octet of

$$: \ddot{\underset{..}{I}} — \overset{.}{\underset{..}{I}} — \ddot{\underset{..}{I}} :$$

(III)

valence electrons; therefore when iodine accepts an electron pair from a Lewis base one iodine atom must accommodate five electron pairs around itself (III). Iodine atoms accept a fifth electron pair much more readily than the lighter halogens. This may be true because of the large size of iodine or because its vacant $5d$ orbitals are not much higher in energy than the valence $5p$ orbitals. Iodine vapor and solutions of iodine in nonbasic solvents such as carbon tetrachloride are violet in color. Iodine associated with a Lewis base or dissolved in a basic solvent has a characteristic red to brown color, like that of aqueous triiodide solutions.

Organic molecules containing carbon—carbon double bonds can function as Lewis bases with iodine. Solutions of iodine in both cyclohexene and benzene are red and contain adducts of the organic molecules and iodine (IV). These compounds are called *charge transfer* or *π-complexes;* the bonding in them cannot be adequately described with Lewis dot structures.

Strong bases such as hydroxide ion and amines also presumably form adducts with iodine. However, the reaction does not stop at the adduct stage, and dissociation of iodine occurs (6-24).

$$II + OH^- \rightarrow [IIOH^-] \rightarrow I^- + IOH \qquad (6\text{-}24)$$

The halogens exhibit positive oxidation states in their com-

(IV)

pounds with more electronegative elements. These compounds contain largely covalent bonds and chemists do not believe they contain halogen cations. However, there are several compounds of iodine which are perhaps best described as salts of I^+ and I^{3+}. Similar compounds which may contain Cl^+ and Br^+ are also known. That iodine forms more of these compounds is in line with its position in the periodic table and its more metallic nature. The best-known such compound is $I(C_5H_5N)_2NO_3$ (V). This compound is prepared by adding iodine to a chloroform solution containing silver nitrate and the amine pyridine (C_5H_5N) (6-25). This com-

$$I_2 + AgNO_3 + 2NC_5H_5 \xrightarrow{\text{CHCl}_3} I(NC_5H_5)_2NO_3 + AgI \quad (6\text{-}25)$$

pound has a formula very similar to the nitrate salt of a well-characterized complex ion of Ag^+, $Ag(C_5H_5N)_2NO_3$. This compound is analogous to the more familiar complex ion $Ag(NH_3)_2^+$. Solutions of the I^+ complex in suitable solvents conduct electricity, and when electrolyzed yield iodine at the cathode. These pieces of evidence suggest the compound is ionic and dissociates into $I(NC_5H_5)_2^+$ and NO_3^- ions in solution. The corresponding chlorine and bromine compounds can also be prepared.

Compounds whose properties suggest that they may contain I^{3+} have also been prepared. Two examples are iodine triacetate, $I(C_2H_3O_2)_3$, and iodine(III) perchlorate, $I(ClO_4)_3$. Solutions of these compounds yield iodine at the cathode when electrolyzed; this indicates that iodine moves as a positive ion. Neither the X^+ nor I^{3+} salts can exist in water and in general they are reactive oxidizing agents.

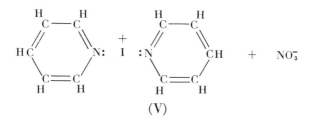

(V)

6-5 METAL HALIDES

Sodium chloride, ordinary table salt, is certainly the most common and familiar halogen compound. This white, crystalline, high-melting, high-boiling, water-soluble solid is the prime example of a salt to most of us. The salt-like behavior is common to many of the metal halides, particularly the mono-(MX) and dihalides (MX$_2$). Most of these have crystalline lattices in which nearest neighbors of each metal are halogens and the nearest neighbors of each halogen are metals (see Figures 2-3 and 5-2). Moreover, each atom is completely surrounded by atoms of the opposite kind.

There is considerable evidence that the metals are present essentially as metal ions in most of these compounds and that the halogens exist as halide ions. These substances are nonconducting at room temperature, but are good electrical conductors at their melting points. The melting points and the electrical conductivities of the metal halides help to differentiate salt-like from molecular halides. Table 6-3 presents melting points and relative con-

Table 6–3
Melting Points and Relative Conductivities[a] of Some Metal Chlorides

MX	M.p., °C	Cond.	MX$_2$	M.p., °C	Cond.
LiCl	614	166	BeCl$_2$	405	0.1
NaCl	800	134	MgCl$_2$	714	29
KCl	770	104	CaCl$_2$	782	52

MX$_3$	M.p., °C	Cond.	MX$_4$	M.p., °C	Cond.
AlCl$_3$	193	10^{-5}			
ScCl$_3$	939	15	TiCl$_4$	-30	0.0

[a] Electrical conductivities at the melting point of each substance.

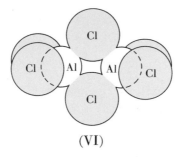

(VI)

ductivities of a few metal halides. The lightest metals in each family and the metals exhibiting the greatest positive charge clearly give the lowest melting and least conducting halides.

The changes in melting points and conductivities are reflected in the structures of the compounds. Titanium tetrachloride has a structure like that of carbon tetrachloride in which the chlorine atoms are tetrahedrally arranged about the central less electronegative atom. These molecules condense into a molecular lattice in which the primary forces are van der Waals interactions. Gaseous aluminum chloride has an interesting dimeric structure (VI). Vapors of other volatile metal trihalides contain molecules with similar structures. In these molecules some chlorines are attached to two metals. They link the molecule together and are called *bridging atoms*. Halogen bridges are common and important in metal halide chemistry. In the solid state aluminum chloride has an entirely different structure, one which is related to that of sodium chloride. However, since there is but one aluminum for three chlorines, only one third of the "sodium" sites in the lattice are occupied. The absence of cations in these sites markedly diminishes the attractions which bind the lattice together and accounts for its low melting point.

The metal halides with low melting points and conductivities react with water (hydrolyze) to generate H^+ and hydroxy compounds. Borderline salt-like halides such as beryllium and aluminum chlorides hydrolyze only partially (6-26, 6-27), whereas for all

$$BeCl_2 + H_2O \overset{H_2O}{\rightleftharpoons} BeOH^+ + 2Cl^- + H^+ \qquad (6\text{-}26)$$

$$AlCl_3 + H_2O \overset{H_2O}{\rightleftarrows} AlOH^{2+} + 3Cl^- + H^+ \qquad (6\text{-}27)$$

molecular metal halides the hydrolysis is complete (6-28, 6-29) and normally rapid. *Hydrolysis* is the reverse of an acid base re-

$$TiCl_4 + 2H_2O \rightarrow TiO_2 \cdot xH_2O(s) + 4H^+ + 4Cl^- \qquad (6\text{-}28)$$

$$2NbCl_5 + 5H_2O \rightarrow Nb_2O_5 \cdot xH_2O(s) + 10H^+ + 10Cl^- \qquad (6\text{-}29)$$

action. Hydrolysis occurs when the reaction of a salt with water yields either a weak acid or weak base. The extent of hydrolysis is determined by the weakness of the acid or base formed. As a consequence the behavior observed in reactions (6-28) and (6-29) (and in hydrolyses of other halides) is consistent with the generalizations on the basicity of hydroxides and oxides given in Section 1-3. The hydroxides $BeOH^+$ and $AlOH^{2+}$ are weak bases and therefore some hydrolysis occurs. The Be^{2+} and Al^{3+} ions are smaller and more highly charged than ions such as Ca^{2+} and Na^+, which form halide salts that do not hydrolyze and have high melting points. The Ti^{4+} and Nb^{5+} ions are both highly charged and small. Their oxides (and hydroxides) are very poor bases and hence hydrolysis of titanium(IV) and niobium(V) halides is complete.

The silver halides are particularly important metal halogen compounds. Silver chloride, bromide, and iodide are quite insoluble and their precipitation (6-30) is frequently used in the

$$Ag^+(\text{aqueous}) + Br^-(\text{aqueous}) \rightarrow AgBr(s) \qquad (6\text{-}30)$$

analysis of both halides and silver. Silver bromide is used in large quantities as the light-sensitive component of photographic film. Silver chloride, bromide, and iodide all darken when exposed to sunlight as a result of photochemical decomposition and the resulting formation of dark, finely divided silver metal. Silver is not a very electropositive metal; silver-chlorine, -bromine, and -iodine bonds have considerable covalent character. The presence of covalent bonding in these silver halides is usually cited as the reason for the insolubility of AgX salts in water. Silver fluoride and all the alkali metal halides are water soluble and it is generally conceded that the bonding in these solids is primarily ionic.

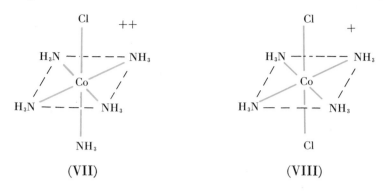

(VII)   (VIII)

Halide ions not only form binary compounds with metals, but are often present in complex ions. A few of these such as AlF_6^{3-} occur in nature (in this case as Na_3AlF_6, the mineral cryolite); most have been prepared in the laboratory. Fluoride ion forms complexes with a number of metals and nonmetals; some of these have been mentioned earlier. Other halide complexes include $AgCl_2^-$, some of which forms when Ag^+ is precipitated with too large an excess of chloride ion (6-31). The hexachloroplatinate(IV) ion ($PtCl_6^{2-}$) forms a relatively water-insoluble

$$AgCl(s) + Cl^-(aqueous) \xrightarrow{H_2O} AgCl_2^-(aqueous) \qquad (6\text{-}31)$$

salt with potassium and can be used to analyze for this ion. Early interest in coordination chemistry was aroused by the preparation of a series of cobalt(III) complexes containing ammonia and chloride. Two of these are $Co(NH_3)_5Cl^{2+}$ (VII) and $Co(NH_3)_4Cl_2^+$ (VIII).

SUPPLEMENTARY READING LIST

R. T. Sanderson, "Principles of Halogen Chemistry," *J. Chem. Ed.*, **41**, 361 (1964).

A. H. W. Aten, Jr., "The Chemistry of Astatine" *in* H. J. Emeleus and A. G. Sharpe (eds.), *Advances in Inorganic Chemistry and*

Radiochemistry, Vol. 6, p. 207, Academic, New York, 1964.

E. K. Hyde, "Astatine and Francium," *J. Chem. Ed.*, **36**, 15 (1959).

R. R. Holmes, "Ionic and Molecular Halides of the Phosphorus Family," *J. Chem. Ed.*, **40**, 125 (1963).

E. H. Wiebenga, E. E. Havinga, and K. H. Boswijk, "Structures of Interhalogen Compounds and Polyhalides" *in* H. J. Emeleus and A. G. Sharpe (eds.), *Advances in Inorganic Chemistry and Radiochemistry*, Vol. 3, p. 91, Academic, New York, 1961.

M. Schmeisser and K. Brandle, "Oxides and Oxyfluorides of the Halogens," *ibid.*, Vol. 5, p. 42, 1963.

L. J. Andrews and R. M. Keefer, "Molecular Complexes of Halogens," *ibid.*, Vol. 3, p. 91, 1961. A discussion of adducts of organic molecules with iodine and other halogens.

J. J. Katz and I. Sheft, "Halides of Actinide Elements," *ibid.*, Vol. 2, p. 195, 1961.

J. Arotsky and M. C. R. Symons, "Halogen Cations," *Quart. Rev. London*, **16**, 282 (1962).

W. L. Jolly, "The Use of Oxidation Potentials in Inorganic Chemistry," *J. Chem. Ed.*, **43**, 198 (1966).

(See Chapter VII for a general reading list.)

PROBLEMS

1. Contrast the properties of fluorine and fluorine compounds with those of chlorine and chlorine compounds. Note at least three similarities and three differences in properties.

2. Which oxidation states of sulfur would be predicted to be the most common? Look in a general chemistry text to check how valid your prediction is.

3. Predict the formulas of the compounds of sulfur with barium, indium, arsenic, oxygen, and chlorine. Look in a handbook of chemistry to see whether the predicted compounds are common enough to be included.

4. Suggest methods for preparing these compounds: AgF_2, VF_4 ($F_2 + V \rightarrow VF_5$ as the primary product), $NaClO_3$, $KClO$, $K_2H_3IO_6$, ICl, ICl_4^-, and $AlBr_3$.

5. Predict the acid dissociation constants of H_5IO_6, $H_4IO_6^-$, and $H_3IO_6^{2-}$.

6. Name the following compounds: $AgIO_4$, $HBrO_3$, HI, $Ca(ClO)_2$, Al_2I_6, CsI_3.

7. Suggest explanations for these observations: (a) Iodide ion is a better reducing agent than F^-, Cl^-, and Br^-. (b) The elemental halogens do not occur in nature. (c) The reaction of water with NCl_3 yields $HOCl$ and NH_3, whereas PCl_3 yields $P(OH)_3$ and HCl.

8. Suggest methods which would allow you to distinguish between these substances: (a) $NaCl$ and NaI; (b) $NaClO$ and $NaClO_4$; (c) $NaClO_3$ and $NaIO_3$.

9. The standard electrode potentials for the reduction of the oxyanions of the halogens to the halogen by hydrogen in acidic solution are given below. (For example, $2ClO_3^- + 5H_2 | 2H^+ \rightarrow Cl_2 + 6H_2O$ $E^0 - 1.47$ V.)

	HOX	XO_3^-	XO_4^-
Cl	1.63	1.47	1.39
Br	1.59	1.52	
I	1.45	1.20	1.3 (H_5IO_6)
At	1.0	1.4	

(a) The oxidizing ability of these species does not follow a simple periodic pattern. Arrange the HOX species in order of increasing oxidizing ability; do the same for the XO_3^- ions.

(b) Arrange the oxyanions in which the halogen exhibits the $+7$ oxidation state in order of increasing oxidizing ability. Where do BrO_4^- and $H_3AtO_6^{2-}$ fit in this correlation?

(c) Note and comment on any trends which are apparent in the correlations made in (a) and (b).

(d) Arrange the oxyanions of each halogen in order of increasing oxidizing ability. Note any trends.

10. In acidic solution which of these reactions may occur? Base your answers on data in Table 6–1.

(a) $Cl_2 + H_2O \rightarrow HOCl + H^+ + Cl^-$

(b) $3HOCl \rightarrow HClO_2 + Cl_2 + H_2O$

(c) $2HClO_2 \rightarrow HOCl + H^+ + ClO_3^-$

(d) $2ClO_3^- + H^+ \rightarrow HClO_2 + ClO_4^-$

(e) $I_2 + H_2O \rightarrow HOI + H^+ + I^-$

(f) $10HOI \rightarrow 2IO_3^- + 4I_2 + 2H^+ + 4H_2O$

(g) $3IO_3^- + 4H_2O + 3H^+ \rightarrow 2H_5IO_6 + HOI$

(h) $At_2 + H_2O \rightarrow HOAt + H^+ + At^-$

(i) $10HOAt \rightarrow 2AtO_3^- + 4At_2 + 2H^+ + 4H_2O$

11. In basic solution, which of the reactions corresponding to those in Problem 10 may occur?

12. Of the reactions in Problems 10 and 11 that may occur, two proceed at slow rates. Hypochlorite ion disproportionates very slowly at room temperature but fairly rapidly at 75°C. Chlorate ion disproportionates very slowly even at 100°C. Therefore, when chlorine is dissolved in a basic solution at 25.0°C what are the primary products? What are the products at 90°C? What are the primary products when iodine is dissolved in an aqueous basic solution?

13. Calculate the equilibrium constant at 25°C for reaction 10(a). The total solubility of chlorine in water at 25°C is 0.091 mole/liter. Calculate the molar concentrations of Cl_2, Cl^-, and HOCl in this aqueous chlorine solution. Calculate the concentration of Cl_2, Cl^-, and HOCl if the H^+ concentration of the solution were fixed at 1.0 M. Note that although in Problem 10 we predicted that reaction 10(a) does not occur in strongly acidic solution, in fact about 1% of the chlorine is converted into products under these conditions.

						H											He
											B	C	N	O	F	Ne
													P	S	Cl	Ar
														Se	Br	Kr
	VII														I	Xe
															At	Rn

Other Nonmetals

B OOKS HAVE BEEN WRITTEN about the chemistry of many elements. Therefore a short text cannot hope to describe adequately the properties of one element, much less all the nonmetals. Chapters in this book have tried to introduce the reader to some interesting or important features of the chemistry of hydrogen, nitrogen, the halogens, and their compounds. In the process compounds of other elements have been discussed, but space does not allow a more complete presentation of their chemistry.

A large number of sources of information are available to persons who wish to know more about the chemistry of any element. A quest for such information normally starts with an introduction such as that which may be found in any of several general or advanced inorganic texts. More specialized and detailed information is available in several series of books which have compiled much of the chemistry of every element. Other books are available which contain reviews on specific kinds of compounds or on the chemistry of individual elements. A thorough study ultimately leads to research journals which discuss in detail specific systems. The latest information is available only in journals. A reading list follows which should aid the reader desiring to make a serious study of some element or compound.

READING LIST

Examples of textbooks which contain a summary of the chemistry of most elements:

R. A. Plane and R. E. Hester, *Elements of Inorganic Chemistry*, Benjamin, New York, 1965.
F. A. Cotton and G. Wilkinson, *Advanced Inorganic Chemistry*, 2nd ed., Wiley (Interscience), New York, 1966.
R. B. Heslop and P. L. Robinson, *Inorganic Chemistry*, Elsevier, London, 1960.
J. Kleinberg, W. J. Argersinger, and E. Griswold, *Inorganic Chemistry*, Heath, Boston, 1960.

Most general chemistry textbooks contain sufficient information about the common elements to provide a useful start in the study of an element.

Books which present detailed information on most elements:

M. C. Sneed, J. L. Maynard, and R. C. Brasted, *Comprehensive Inorganic Chemistry*, 8 vols., Van Nostrand, New York, 1953–1961.
J. W. Mellor, *A Comprehensive Treatise on Inorganic and Theoretical Chemistry*, 16 vols., plus supplements, Longmans Green, London, 1922–1964.
N. V. Sidgwick, *Chemical Elements and Their Compounds*, 2 vols., Oxford, London, 1950.
I. M. Kolthoff, P. J. Elving, E. B. Sandell, *Treatise on Analytical Chemistry, Part II; Analytical Chemistry of the Elements*, 9 vols., Wiley (Interscience), New York, 1961–1964.
Gmelins Handbuch der Anorganichen Chemie, over 60 vols., plus supplements, Verlag Chemie, Weinheim/Bergstrasse, 1924—.
P. Pascal, *Nouveau Traité de Chemie Minérale*, 20 vols., Masson, Paris, 1956–1960.

Books which describe the syntheses of inorganic compounds:

Inorganic Syntheses, 7 vols., McGraw-Hill, New York, 1939–1963.

G. Brauer, *Handbook of Preparative Inorganic Chemistry*, 2 vols., Academic, New York (in English); Ferdinand Enke Verlag, Stuttgart (in German), 1962.

W. L. Jolly (ed.), *Preparative Inorganic Reactions*, 2 vols., Wiley (Interscience), New York, 1964—.

W. G. Palmer, *Experimental Inorganic Chemistry*, Cambridge, New York, 1954.

G. G. Schlessinger, *Inorganic Laboratory Preparations*, Chemical Publishing, New York, 1962.

H. F. Walton, *Inorganic Preparations*, Prentice-Hall, Englewood Cliffs, N.J., 1948.

Selected books which describe the chemistry of individual elements, groups of elements, or classes of compounds:

W. L. Jolly, *The Chemistry of the Nonmetals*, Prentice-Hall, Englewood Cliffs, N.J., 1966.

D. M. Yost and H. Russell, Jr., *Systematic Chemistry of the Fifth and Sixth Group Nonmetallic Elements*, Prentice-Hall, Englewood Cliffs, N.J., 1944.

J. R. Van Wazer, *Phosphorus and Its Compounds*, Wiley (Interscience), New York, 1958.

M. Ardon, *Oxygen: Elementary Forms and Hydrogen Peroxide*, Benjamin, New York, 1965.

E. M. Larsen, *Transitional Elements*, Benjamin, New York, 1965.

F. Basolo and R. C. Johnson, *Coordination Chemistry: The Chemistry of Metal Complexes*, Benjamin, New York, 1964.

Other books which are useful in the study of the chemistry of nonmetals:

M. E. Weeks, *Discovery of the Elements*, Chemical Education Publishing, Easton, Pa., 1945.

J. O. Edwards, *Inorganic Reaction Mechanisms: An Introduction*, Benjamin, New York, 1964.

A. F. Wells, *Structural Inorganic Chemistry*, 3rd ed., Clarendon, Oxford, 1962.

H. J. Emeleus and A. G. Sharpe (eds.), *Advances in Inorganic Chemistry and Radiochemistry*, 7 vols., Academic, New York, 1959—.

F. A. Cotton (ed.), *Progress in Inorganic Chemistry*, 7 vols., Wiley (Interscience), New York, 1959—.

Index